CESWI-4

explained

A guide to the development, understanding and use of the

Civil Engineering Specification for the Water Industry

by

HAYDN WHITE

with Appendices compiled

by Brian Spark

WRc PUBLICATIONS, 1994

The terminology used in this book, including the use of capital letters, is consistent with that in the ICE Conditions of Contract (Sixth Edition), the WSA Civil Engineering Specification for the Water Industry (Fourth Edition) and the ICE Standard Method of Measurement (Third Edition). Any interpretation offered in the book as to the meaning of any of these documents is not an official interpretation and should not be used as such in connection with any dispute arising out of a contract.

This guide and the statements made or opinions expressed therein is published on the understanding that the author is solely responsible for the opinions expressed in it and that its publication does not necessarily imply that such statements and or opinions are or reflect the views or opinions of the Water Services Association of England and Wales.

Published by:

WRc plc,
Henley Road
Medmenham
Marlow
Bucks
SL7 2HD

The Civil Engineering Specification for the Water Industry (Fourth Edition) is published by WRc on behalf of the Water Services Association.

© WRc plc, October 1994

ISBN 1 898920 03 6

FOREWORD

BY THE CHAIRMAN OF THE WSA WATER SERVICES MANAGEMENT GROUP

I appointed Haydn White to Yorkshire Water's head office in 1974 and until he opted for early retirement last year he remained at the centre of things, not only in Yorkshire but increasingly on the national and international scenes.

One aspect of his work before joining Yorkshire Water's privatisation team was day-to-day responsibility for the authority's contract procedures and Employer functions where disputes arose. This, together with his unrivalled experience of CESWI, as we all call it, makes him uniquely qualified to write this book.

I was aware that Haydn did not intend to rest on his laurels after leaving Yorkshire Water, continuing among other things with his work on national and international standards of interest to the water industry. However, as Chairman of the WSA Water Services Management Group I was very pleased to see that he has found time to put his long experience with CESWI down on paper.

The publication of CESWI-4 demonstrates the on-going commitment of the water service companies and the statutory water companies to the idea of a standard specification. I am therefore very happy to commend the book to all those involved with the preparation, supervision and construction of the water industry's civil engineering contracts.

A I WARD

London, 1994

2

PREFACE

It seems that I was the youngest member of the original CESWI working group by a good many years - so much so that by October 1985 I was the only one left!

When eventually I too opted for early retirement at the end of March 1993, work on CESWI-4 was just getting into full swing. And as I settled into what I fondly thought would be a more relaxed style of life, it occurred to me that almost 20 years of unique experience with CESWI ought not to go to waste.

The result is this book, which I hope those using CESWI will find helpful, readable and informative. I am conscious that much of it falls into the category of a history lesson, but this is necessary for an understanding of what lies behind CESWI and how it fits into the contractual scene.

One measure of success will be the number of times the reader exclaims: *"So that's why......... !"*

Thanks are due to my successor as Chairman of the CESWI Working Group, Brian Spark of Anglian Water, for drafting the Appendices. Also to WRc's Colin Tregoing, the Group's Technical Secretary, for casting such a thorough and professional eye over the text.

The book is affectionately dedicated to my friends and former colleagues on the working group that developed the first edition of CESWI. Sadly, not all are still with us, while the rest have since retired, but their specification stands as testimony to the knowledge, commitment and skills that were brought to bear.

HAYDN WHITE

Leeds, 1994

CONTENTS

ABBREVIATIONS

ASTM	American Society for Testing Materials
BBA	British Board of Agrément
BRE	Building Research Establishment
BSI	British Standards Institution
CAWC	Central Advisory Water Committee
CCSJC	Conditions of Contract Standing Joint Committee
CCTV	Closed Circuit Television
CE	Communauté Européene
CEN	Comité Européen de Normalisation
CENELEC	Comité Européen de Normalisation Electrotechnique
CESMM	Civil Engineering Standard Method of Measurement
CESWI	Civil Engineering Specification for the Water Industry
CIRIA	Construction Industry Research and Information Association
CPA	Concrete Pipe Association
CPD	Construction Products Directive (89/106/EEC)
DAME	Documents Are Mutually Explanatory
DD	Draft for Development
DN	Diamètre Nominal (Nominal Diameter)
DoE	Department of the Environment
DTI	Department of Trade and Industry
DTp	Department of Transport
EFTA	European Free Trade Association
EN	Europäische Norm (European Standard)
Fifth Edition	Fifth Edition of the ICE Conditions of Contract
FWR	Foundation for Water Research
ggbs	Ground granulated blastfurnace slag
HAUC	Highway Authorities and Utilities Committee
HMSO	Her Majesty's Stationery Office
ICE	Institution of Civil Engineers
IGN	Information and Guidance Note
JCC	Joint Contracts Committee
NACCB	National Accreditation Council for Certification Bodies
NJHSCWS	National Joint Health and Safety Committee for the Water Service

NRA	National Rivers Authority
NWC	National Water Council
pfa	Pulverized-fuel ash
PJA	Pipe Jacking Association
prEN	Draft European Standard
QAWG	Quality Assurance Working Group
SADWSS	Scottish Association of Directors of Water and Sewerage Services
SDD	Scottish Development Department
Sixth Edition	Sixth Edition of the ICE Conditions of Contract
SRM	Sewerage Rehabilitation Manual
STCSWM	Standing Technical Committee on Sewers and Water Mains
SWMC	Sewers and Water Mains Committee
WAA	Water Authorities' Association
WCA	Water Companies' Association
WDA	Well Drillers' Association
WICS	Water Industry Certification Scheme
WIs	Water Industry specification
WSA	Water Services Association of England and Wales
WSMG	Water Services Management Group

1 - ORIGINS

In a historic 1971 Circular[1] the Department of the Environment (DoE) announced that the Government *"believe the time has come to bring together, under all-purpose management structures, all aspects of the hydrological cycle, literally from the source to the tap"*. It is not known what the Almighty thought about the idea relative to the non-terrestrial part of the cycle, but those employed in the waste water side of the industry were intrigued to read on and find out whether the proposals would, indeed, be limited "from the source to the tap", or whether the Circular's author simply came from a drinking water background and had forgotten to remove his blinkers.

The idea for all-purpose regional water authorities in England and Wales was developed in a Central Advisory Water Committee (CAWC) report[2], published in April 1971. This, together with the conclusions in the DoE Circular, formed the basis of the Government's eventual proposals to the House of Commons, which finally saw the light of day as the Water Act 1973[3]. Students of the terrestrial hydrological cycle were relieved to find that Parliament had taken a broader view than "literally from the source to the tap", but were puzzled to note that the new water authorities' management of the water cycle would actually cease at the tap, then recommence at the public sewer!

In some parts of the country, however, the situation was to be a little more complex than foreseen by the CAWC report. The Committee had envisaged that all-purpose regional water authorities would acquire the 31 statutory water companies (29 in England, and 2 partly in England and partly in Wales), which at that time accounted for about 22 per cent of the total water supplied by statutory undertakers. However, it was made clear in the 1971 Circular that: *"In the Government's view, consideration of the desirable form of organization within the public sector must be distinguished from proposals for a further increase in the size of the public sector. There must be a strong presumption against any such proposal. The company undertakings are in general viable and efficient and the Government see a continuing role for them as agents of the regional water authorities in the field of water supply"*. Viewed from a time when the water authorities themselves have been privatised, one can but admire the foresight!

It is appropriate here to mention one other significant complication that arose when the Government's proposals were passing through Parliament. The 1971 Circular had envisaged that all sewerage functions relative to public sewers would be transferred to, and exercised by, the new water authorities but, as we have just seen, local authorities were to continue to have local sewerage functions - that is, in relation to private sewers and drains.

There was an outcry among local authorities at the prospect of losing "public" sewerage services, which are so closely linked to infrastructure development. The Secretary of State saw the force of the arguments put forward by those representing the local authorities and attempts were made to create a more significant demarcation than "public" sewers on the one hand and "private" sewers and drains on the other. All efforts to come up with a meaningful definition of "trunk" public sewers (which alone, it was suggested, should become the responsibility of the water authorities, the remaining public sewers staying under local authority control) failed and the Secretary of State was reluctant to depart further from the principle of English and Welsh river basin management by multifunctional authorities.

The political solution was to make it the duty of each new water authority to endeavour to make arrangements with those local authorities in its area that the Local Government Act 1972 had envisaged would become sewerage authorities, for the discharge of many of the former's sewerage functions by the latter. Such "arrangements" were commonly referred to as "agencies", but this was a popular misconception, for a principal is usually free to choose his own agent and there was to be no such right in the case of sewerage functions.

The 1973 Act led to ten water authorities coming into operation on 1 April 1974. Nine regional water authorities were created in England, based broadly on the areas of the old river authorities, whilst the grandly named "Welsh National Water Development Authority" was established in Wales. The latter had its origins not only in the political wish to recognize the principality, but also in the fact that a great deal of water, though impounded in Wales, was transmitted over the border into England. However, the grandiose title did not find long-lasting favour with the sensible Welsh.

The *"need for a body to speak for the industry as a whole, and to provide central services for its benefit"* had been recognized in the 1971 Circular. Accordingly, the 1973 Act also established the National Water Council (NWC), it also coming fully into operation on 1 April 1974, along with the ten new water authorities.

As might be imagined, the task of transferring most of the water services of England and Wales from a wide variety of public bodies into the new multifunctional authorities was an enormous one. Much of the planning and co-ordination fell to the DoE and the Directorate General of Water Engineering produced a comprehensive "Technical Brief" for each of the proposed water authorities, so that the incoming members and senior management of each authority could familiarize themselves with their area, the existing provision of functional services and the capital expenditure programmes inherited from the outgoing bodies.

The new authorities had the benefit of another document produced at the DoE's instigation. In June 1972, as the Government's proposals for reorganizing the water and sewage services of England and Wales were passing through Parliament, the Secretary of State for the Environment appointed a committee under the Chairmanship of Sir George Ogden, the then Town Clerk of Manchester, *"to consider possible forms of management structure with a view to producing guidance on this matter for regional water authorities"*.

The Committee's subsequent report[4] was published in June 1973 and one of its main recommendations was that each water authority should have a Director of Operations. In discussing the responsibilities of such a post the report said: *"In all cases he will be ultimately responsible not only for the operation of existing water supply treatment and distribution facilities, sewerage and sewage treatment facilities, and river management undertakings at divisional levels, but also for ensuring the availability of such services as are necessary to maintain the effective operation of these facilities and undertakings. In addition he will be responsible for the design, construction and commissioning of the programme of works agreed by the authority. This may be undertaken centrally, or in the divisions."*

Senior appointments for the new water authorities were made during the latter part of 1973. For the most part these were consistent with the guidance of the Ogden report as regards management structures and in every case the recommendation to appoint a Director of Operations was followed.

Thus, on Monday 29 April 1974 ten Directors of Operations, together with representatives of the NWC and DoE, met for the first time as the NWC Directors of Operations' Group. On the subject of technical standardization they quickly and unanimously agreed[5] that they were *"in favour of the setting up of a working group serviced by NWC/DoE with the remit to consider the drawing up of specifications for the water service"*. Although the minute did not need to say so, it is appropriate to point out that the decision applied only to the "water service" as provided by the new water authorities in England and Wales.

The Directors of Operations lost no time in nominating their representatives to the "Working Group on Standard Specifications" (as it was originally called) and it held its first meeting at the NWC's offices at Queen Anne's Gate in London on Friday, 5 July 1974.

2 - FUNDAMENTALS

The NWC working group's first task was to come to grips with two fundamental issues: Was the expertise gathered together on the basis of Directors of Operations' nominations sufficiently comprehensive? And what form of specification would be most appropriate for the reorganized water industry's civil engineering works in the latter part of the twentieth century?

It happened that both of these issues had been recently addressed by a working party set up in 1970 by the Scottish Development Department (SDD) to prepare a standard specification for water and sewerage schemes in Scotland. The work took two years and the resulting specification[6] was published early in 1973, the Scottish working party's response to the two issues identified above being as follows:

1.   Membership was extended to include representatives of organizations reflecting the interests and expertise of contractors, consulting engineers, county engineers and municipal engineers; and

2.   A traditional "method" type of specification was drawn up, in which the Contractor often had to follow a prescribed way of constructing parts of the Works.

PAYING THE PIPER

The NWC working group took the view, with the full backing of Directors of Operations, that the specification for use in England and Wales should be drawn up by representatives of those who would be paying for and sanctioning the associated capital works. As might be expected, this prompted considerable discussion on the positions of the statutory water companies, and of those local authorities who, from 1 April 1974, had begun to exercise many of the new water authorities' sewerage functions. A case for the representation of each on the working group had been made in various quarters. It was eventually concluded that the former ought to be represented by the Water Companies' Association (WCA), but that the latter should not be directly represented on the working group, since their standing under the Water Act 1973 was not analogous to that of the statutory water companies.

Having decided that a client with sufficient expertise to do so should be entitled to decide on a specification appropriate to his needs, the working group was left to consider whether such expertise existed around the table. Directors of Operations had made it clear that they wanted a civil engineering specification for each of the main functions for which the water authorities were now responsible. That is to say, not only water supply and sewerage (as covered by the SDD specification) but also sewage treatment and, insofar as was practicable, river engineering. The working group was fortunate to have the benefit of considerable expertise in all of the required functions.

Of course, it would have been less than sensible to adopt a wholly insular approach to writing the specification. Therefore, the working group made an early decision that, as and when a full draft was available, it would be circulated for the widest possible comment, not only to the water authorities and statutory water companies, but also to professional bodies, trade associations and other interested parties.

CALLING THE TUNE

The working group had considerable misgivings about drafting a traditional "method" type of specification and the roots of this lay in the publication of the Fifth Edition of the ICE Conditions of Contract[7] in June 1973. The concerns, indeed much of the working group's philosophy, were summed up in the following statement[8] by Sir William Harris, Chairman of the Joint Contracts Committee (JCC) responsible for the new Fifth Edition:

> "It is the right and the duty of the Employer to decide and by his Engineer, to design and specify that which is to be done and it is the Employer's duty to allow the Contractor to do that which is to be done without hindrance.
>
> It is the duty of the Contractor to do what the Contract requires to be done, as designed and specified by the Engineer, but, subject to any specific requirement in the Contract, it is his right and duty to decide the manner in which he will do it.
>
> If there are to be exceptional cases where the Contractor is to decide what to do, or to design what is to be done, or where the Employer or the Engineer is to decide how the work is to be done, the Contract must expressly provide for this and for the necessary financial consequences for the protection of the Contractor."

The working group was unable to reconcile the words of Sir William Harris, and the corresponding provisions of the new Fifth Edition, with drafting a traditional "method" type of specification and so it opted for one written primarily in terms of the performance required, leaving the Contractor, so far as possible, free to decide his method of working.

3 - ICE CONDITIONS

The fundamental assumption that the proposed specification would be used in connection with unamended ICE Conditions of Contract had several far-reaching implications, not least among them was the size of the challenge that the working group quickly realized it was facing. Several existing documents were considered for use or modification, the SDD specification being a prime candidate (indeed, Mr S C Agnew, Chairman of the SDD working party, met the working group to explain the background to that particular specification, which predated the Fifth Edition), but each one was written in the traditional "method" style, as opposed to the "performance" approach that the working group had decided to adopt. The new specification was going to have to be written from scratch !

Successive editions of the ICE Conditions have defined the "Specification" as:

> "1 (1) (f) 'Specification' means the specification referred to in the Tender and any modification thereof or addition thereto as may from time to time be furnished or approved in writing by the Engineer."

In itself, such a bland statement had no significance for the proposed specification, but the same could not be said about other aspects of the ICE Conditions. The entire document had to be written against the following background:

THE ENGINEER

Like its predecessors, the Fifth Edition did not have specific clauses dealing with the duties, authority and impartiality of the Engineer. Nevertheless, it continued the central tenet of earlier editions that, subject to arbitration, the impartial Engineer held unfettered powers, not least as regards his right (indeed, duty) to certify payment to the Contractor, whether or not the Employer was content to make a particular payment. The functions of the Engineer were neatly summed up in a 1977 Guidance Note[9] issued by the ICE Conditions of Contract Standing Joint Committee (CCSJC), successor to the JCC:

> "The Engineer is appointed by the Employer to administer the Contract and to that end is conferred with powers and duties which are vested in the Engineer and in none other.
>
> While the Engineer has a duty to act as the agent of the Employer and supervise the construction of the Works to ensure that the Contractor constructs them in accordance with the Contract, of no less importance are those functions which require the Engineer to make decisions relating to the allocation of responsibility for risks, changes made in the course of construction and the time within which the Works are to be constructed. In all aspects of his duties the Engineer is expected to act within the terms of the Contract impartially, honestly and with professional integrity, towards both parties to the Contract."

It is not necessary here to consider the pressures that have been brought to bear in recent years on the role of the Engineer. The working group approached the drafting of the new specification in the light of the Fifth Edition and whatever guidance had been issued by the CCSJC. However, it is perhaps worth noting that, for the first time, the following new provisions were written into the Sixth Edition[10]:

"2 (1) (a) The Engineer shall carry out the duties specified in or necessarily to be implied from the Contract.

(b) The Engineer may exercise the authority specified in or necessarily to be implied from the Contract. If the Engineer is required under the terms of his appointment by the Employer to obtain specific approval of the Employer before exercising any such authority particulars of such requirements shall be those set out in the Appendix to the Form of Tender. Any requisite approval shall be deemed to have been given by the Employer for any such authority exercised by the Engineer."

(c) Except as expressly stated in the Contract the Engineer shall have no authority to amend the Terms and Conditions of the Contract nor to relieve the Contractor of any of his obligations under the Contract."

"2 (8) The Engineer shall except in connection with matters requiring the specific approval of the Employer under sub-clause (1)(b) of the Clause act impartially within the terms of the Contract having regard to all the circumstances."

It is axiomatic that there cannot be an Engineer until there is a contract, because Clause 1(1)(c) of the ICE Conditions requires him to be named in the Contract. Therefore, the working group was careful to distinguish between the roles of those preparing documents for tenderers and the role of the Engineer for the purposes of a contract.

DOCUMENTS ARE MUTUALLY EXPLANATORY

Clause 5 of the ICE Conditions was, and remains, fundamental to the approach taken by the working group when drafting the specification. It reads as follows:

"The several documents forming the Contract are to be taken as mutually explanatory of one another and in case of ambiguities or discrepancies the same shall be explained and adjusted by the Engineer who shall thereupon issue to the Contractor appropriate instructions in writing which shall be regarded as instructions issued in accordance with Clause 13."

How many times have Specifications been written with requirements that purport to cover a subject that is already covered by the ICE Conditions? Only to find that different language is used and the inevitable dispute arises ! The working group resolved that its new document would be confined to matters that were properly for the Specification and not for some other contract document. In this connection it should be noted that the Form of Agreement for use with the ICE Conditions states that:

"The following documents shall be deemed to form and be read and construed as part of this Agreement, namely

(a) the said Tender and the written acceptance thereof
(b) the Drawings
(c) the Conditions of Contract
(d) the Specification
(e) the priced Bill of Quantities"

WORK TO BE TO SATISFACTION OF ENGINEER

Countless Specifications have been written with phrases such as *"to the satisfaction of the Engineer"* or *"in a manner acceptable to the Engineer"* added again and again after successive requirements which the Contractor must observe. The "documents are mutually explanatory (DAME)" rule renders this unnecessary, for Clause 13 of the ICE Conditions includes the following provisions:

> *"(1) Save insofar as it is legally or physically impossible the Contractor shall construct and complete the Works in strict accordance with the Contract to the satisfaction of the Engineer and shall comply with and adhere strictly to the Engineer's instructions on any matter connected therewith (whether mentioned in the Contract or not). The Contractor shall take instructions only from the Engineer or (subject to the limitations referred to in Clause 2) from the Engineer's Representative.*
>
> *(2) The whole of the materials plant and labour to be provided by the Contractor under Clause 8 and the mode manner and speed of construction of the Works are to be of a kind and conducted in a manner acceptable to the Engineer."*

In passing, it is interesting to note that the above sub-clauses have remained unaltered in successive editions of the ICE Conditions. Given the fact that the authors of the Sixth Edition were at pains to replace the term "plant" with the somewhat less elegant *"Contractor's Equipment"*, a rogue *"plant"* appears to have escaped the net and got through to sub-clause (2)!

SPECIFYING THE IMPOSSIBLE

Clause 13(1) of the ICE Conditions provides another means of avoiding disputes, especially on the Site, if the "DAME" rule is observed. Again, over the years countless Specifications have been written that purport to demand the impossible, a classic example being *"pipes shall be laid true to line and level"*. This clearly cannot be done and contractors found themselves in the position of working to the subjective tolerances of individual site staffs. The working group determined not to fall into this trap but, as we shall see later, it was not always successful.

CONFORMING WITH STATUTES

Another common trap for specification writers was to demand, in relation to a particular aspect of the Works, that the Contractor must comply with whatever statute seemed to the writer to be relevant. This was unnecessary, for Clause 26 of successive editions of the ICE Conditions has included (with minor variations in wording) the following provisions:

> *"(3) The Contractor shall ascertain and conform in all respects with the provisions of any general or local Act of Parliament and the Regulations and Bye-laws of any local or other statutory authority which may be applicable to the works and with such rules and regulations of public bodies and companies as aforesaid and shall keep the Employer indemnified against all penalties and liability of every kind for breach of any such Act Regulation or Bye-law. Provided always that*
>
> *(a) the Contractor shall not be required to indemnify the Employer against the consequences of any such breach which is the*

unavoidable result of complying with the Contract or instructions of the Engineer

(b) if the Contract or instructions of the Engineer shall at any time be found not to be in conformity with any such Act Regulation or Bye-law the Engineer shall issue such instructions including the ordering of a variation under Clause 51 as may be necessary to ensure conformity with such Act Regulation or Bye-law and

(c) the Contractor shall not be responsible for obtaining any planning permission which may be necessary in respect of the Permanent Works or any Temporary Works design supplied by the Engineer and the Employer hereby warrants that all the said permissions have been or will in due time be obtained."

Following the "DAME" rule, the working group set out not to refer to any particular statute in its specification. However, it recognized that many statutes were particularly relevant to the construction of water services civil enginnering works and so it resolved to draw attention to these in some form of *aide-mémoire*.

MEASUREMENT

The Fifth Edition included the following Clause:

"57. Except where any statement or general or detailed description of the work in the Bill of Quantities expressly shows to the contrary Bills of Quantities shall be deemed to have been prepared and measurements shall be made according to the procedure set forth in the 'Standard Method of Measurement of Civil Engineering Quantities' issued by the Institution of Civil Engineers and reprinted in 1973 or such later or amended edition thereof as may be stated in the Appendix to the Form of Tender to have been adopted in its preparation notwithstanding any general or local custom."

Both the JCC and the working group were well aware that this reference was to be overtaken by events elsewhere.

4 - CESMM

During the early part of the nineteen seventies, culminating in 1974[11], ICE issued reprints of its *"Standard Method of Measurement of Civil Engineering Quantities"*. Although a metric addendum had been included since 1968, further significant change was resisted by ICE because it had commissioned a new and more radical form of document.

The work was undertaken in 1971 by Dr Martin Barnes under the supervision of a steering committee, this being subsequently enlarged to include representatives of the Association of Consulting Engineers and the Federation of Civil Engineering Contractors. A draft of the new document was widely circulated in 1972 and the final version was published in January 1976. Today the use of CESMM is standard, but its introduction, coming as it did during the time when the working group was drafting its specification, was a radical new approach with which all concerned had to come to terms. It is appropriate, therefore, to quote from the Foreword to that first edition[12] of CESMM, since it had echoes of the approach the working group had decided to take with the advent of the Fifth Edition:

> *"The object of the work has been to make improvements while retaining the good features of the previous edition of the standard method of measurement. The principal improvements sought are*
>
> *a) to standardize the layout and contents of Bills of Quantities prepared according to the standard method of measurement*
>
> *b) to provide a systematic structure of bill items leading to more uniform itemization and description*
>
> *c) to review the subdivision of work into items so that a more sensitive and balanced description of the value of work in a contract is provided*
>
> *d) to take account of new techniques in civil engineering construction and management, their influence on the work itself and on the administration of contracts.*
>
> *"A Bill of Quantities which in essence is no more than a price list of the Permanent Works no longer adequately reflects the many variables in the cost of civil engineering construction which have resulted from the developments in constructional techniques and methods. It has therefore been decided to provide for some additional items of measured work and for other items, entered at the option of the tenderer, directly related to methods of construction.*
>
> *A system of work classification has been adopted as the basis of the method of measurement so that Bills of Quantities can be compiled and used more easily. The system should enable much of the repetitive clerical work associated with the use of Bills of Quantities to be simplified, and make the use of computers easier."*

The system of work classification in the new CESMM was noted by the working group and it was decided that, as far as practicable, the main headings of the specification should follow suit. In May 1976 the group met Dr Martin Barnes and it was agreed that close co-operation was needed in order to avoid omissions or anomolies when CESMM was used in conjunction with the new specification. Dr Barnes expressed the view that it would be a great advantage if, in addition to arranging for the order of the sections and clauses of the specification to be similar to those in CESMM, the same

---

reference numbers, letters and phrasing were to be used. The working group thought that this would be difficult to achieve and was doubtful whether the advantages would be sufficient to justify carrying the principle very far.

There was obviously a clear need for the new specification to reflect the fact that CESMM now existed and once again the group's "DAME" rule raised its head. The first and most fundamental point was that the Bill of Quantities and the Preamble are the proper vehicles for prescribing the methods of assessing payment and whether the Employer or the Contractor should bear specific costs. Therefore, phrases such as "and bear the cost of", traditionally slipped into Specifications after a particular requirement upon the Contractor, were to be avoided.

The question of the Preamble caused much debate in the working group, a significant minority wanting to prepare a standard one for use in connection with the new specification. Arguments as to whether or not this was within the group's remit became irrelevant when the detail of the new CESMM was examined.

Clause 5.2 of CESMM states that:

> "The Bill of Quantities shall be divided into the following sections
>
> (a) List of principal quantities
> (b) Preamble
> (c) Daywork Schedule
> (d) Work items (grouped into parts)
> (e) Grand Summary"

Therefore, although some people had been accustomed to writing the Preamble as a separate document - a sort of link between the Specification and the Bill of Quantities - it was clear that, from now on, it was to be an integral part of the latter and so the working group resolved to leave this to those preparing documents for tenderers.

One of the other new CESMM provisions curtailed protracted discussion in the working group as to what might be an appropriate specification for "rock". Members were greatly relieved to read the following in Clause 5.2:

> "Where excavation, boring or driving is included in the work a
> definition of rock shall be given in the Preamble and this definition
> shall be used for the purposes of measurement."

This requirement was dutifully (nay, gleefully) observed, but in due course members of the working group were to become tired of explaining why their specification omitted "rock"!

As had been foreseen at the meeting with Dr Martin Barnes, a number of "grey" areas came to light, as between the provisions of CESMM and the new specification. Of course, this was understandable in two brand-new documents, each adopting such a radical approach. Under the "DAME" rule the group decided to highlight only those issues where there was some doubt as to whether they were covered by CESMM and it is pleasing to note that many of these were clarified in successive editions of CESMM. The challenge now facing the working group was to devise a system whereby the "grey" areas, together with many other issues outside the specification text, could be relayed to those who would be using the new document.

5 - GUIDANCE

The need for associated guidance had been recognized by others when preparing national specifications. For example, the SDD working party had issued a separate booklet[13] to accompany its specification in 1973.

The working group took the view that physically separate guidance was not particularly user-friendly and decided to explore the possibility of associated guidance being given within the same document as the specification, if necessary alongside the clause to which it related. Of course, the possible legal implications of such an approach were appreciated from the outset, but the group was determined to pursue the idea, notwithstanding a report that the SDD working party had rejected a combined document for fear of the guidance being construed to be part of a contract, in spite of any disclaimer that might be given.

It was decided that the NWC specification should preferably have guidance relevant to a particular clause printed alongside it within a wide margin at the left-hand side of each page. Other guidance would be dealt with accordingly. In addition, it was proposed that the following statement should appear on the page immediately preceeding the actual specification (the significance of the terms "General Notes", "Notes for Guidance" and "Associated Topics" being dealt with later on in this chapter):

> *"The General Notes, clause headings, marginal Notes for Guidance and the accompanying 'Associated Topics' are not part of the Specification, and are not to affect the interpretation either of the Specification or of the other Contract documents."*

It was clearly desirable that the working group should seek legal advice on its proposal that guidance associated with the new specification should be published within the same document and not as a separate one. The senior lawyers of the ten water authorities, and of the NWC, were members of the NWC Legal & Parliamentary Group and so the issue was put to that group in December 1977.

Just as had happened relative to the SDD specification, some concerns were voiced to the effect that, despite any disclaimer that might be given, associated guidance could be construed to be part of a contract if it was published in the same document as the main specification. In the event, however, the Legal & Parliamentary Group finally decided[14] that *"it would be impossible to prevent the explanatory notes reaching contractors, and that they would usefully be incorporated in the specification for the guidance of engineers"*.

Armed with the support of the lawyers, the working group began to examine the most suitable ways of presenting guidance associated with the new specification and, as might be expected with such a radical new approach, there was no shortage of issues where this was felt to be necessary. Overall, it was found that the guidance fell into three categories.

NOTES FOR GUIDANCE

The great majority of issues where guidance was considered appropriate could each be related to a particular clause in the new specification and placed alongside it in the form of marginal notes. These were ascribed roman numerals in order to avoid confusion with the arabic ones used in the specification.

The subtlety (some might even say pedantry) as to why the marginal notes were described as *"Notes for Guidance"*, rather than *"Guidance Notes"*, is sometimes thought to derive from the fact that the document accompanying the SDD specification uses *"Notes for Guidance"*. Sadly, this was not the case.

The NWC/DoE Standing Technical Committee on Sewers and Water Mains (STCSWM) and four specialist subcommittees were established following the 1974 reorganization of the water industry in England and Wales, their memberships being drawn from the UK water industry and from other interested bodies. The subcommittees set about producing a whole series of reports and other documents, Subcommittee No. 4 - "Materials and Standards" (later the Materials and Standards Group) being in the vanguard of this work.

A succession of *"Information and Guidance Notes"* (IGNs) began to be published, initially by NWC but later by the Water Research Centre (WRc), so much so that in December 1982 it became necessary to issue loose-leaf binders to keep them together. At that time the purpose of the IGNs was described[15] as follows:

> *"It is intended that the Notes bring to the attention of engineers additional details and changes of specifications which the water industry, through Subcommittee No. 4 of the STCSWM, have agreed with manufacturers prior to agreement at the British Standards Institution. In consequence, some notes will be descriptive while others will be written as standards and specifications. Nevertheless, it is our intention to develop a consistent presentation in other Notes to ensure that information is in an easily available digestible form, and to update the older notes into the new form as the opportunity arises."*

The proposed system of marginal notes was an ideal vehicle for publicising the IGNs and encouraging their wider use but, in an effort to avoid confusion, the working group decided to use the phrase *"Notes for Guidance"* in connection with its Notes.

The distinction between an IGN that simply gave guidance and one which actually comprised the specification for a particular product was later addressed by the Sewers and Water Mains Committee (SWMC), successor to the STCSWM and having been established by the Water Authorities' Association (WAA), itself the successor to the NWC. In January 1989 the SWMC announced that all specifications produced in its IGN series were to be known henceforth as *"Water Industry Specifications"*.

This created a much clearer picture for those using the two types of document, but it was necessary to cheat a little when referring to *"Water Industry Specifications"* in the specification for civil engineering works. It will be appreciated that the word *"Specification"*, when prefixed with a capital letter, has a particular contractual meaning under the ICE Conditions. Therefore, it was decided that any reference should be to a *"Water Industry specification"* (WIs).

A great many of the Notes for Guidance are aimed at those preparing documents for tenderers and it has to be accepted that, if the guidance is not followed, tenderers (and worse, the Contractor) will be able to point to the discrepancy. The working group took the view that it was up to those preparing tender documents to familiarize themselves with the relevant provisions of one of the documents that was to comprise a contract, just as they should with any of the others. After all, it was quite possible that the requirements of a subsequent contract would be incomplete without the information that a Note For Guidance advised should be given. The Appendices to this book are designed to assist those preparing tender documents, based on the CESWI-4 texts where action is prompted.

ASSOCIATED TOPICS

It turned out there were some issues where guidance was needed but this could not be ascribed to any particular clause. Most of these issues resulted from application of the "DAME" rule, or from the fact that the new specification was written in performance terms. A way had to be found of passing on this type of guidance and so the concept of the *"Associated Topic"* was evolved.

Associated Topics serve the same general purpose as the Notes for Guidance, but in most cases they help to explain why clauses covering particular topics have been omitted from certain Sections of the specification. Where deemed to be necessary, they are placed at the end of the relevant Section.

GENERAL NOTES

Having divided the new specification into Sections that more or less followed the CESMM work classifications, the working group found that there were some Sections where an introductory General Note was unavoidable. In most cases this was where users of the specification needed to understand the background against which a particular Section had been drafted.

It was also decided to include a General Note in the introductory pages to the specification. In view of the radical new approach, the group thought that it would be helpful, not least when the inevitable Supplementary Clauses had to be written for particular contracts, if the principles followed when drafting the main specification were listed.

It was necessary for both of the above types of General Note to be covered by the disclaimer at the beginning of the new specification.

6 - SCOPE

The Directors of Operations' broad remit was that the working group should produce a specification covering the civil engineering content of the four main functions of the reorganized water service - water supply, sewerage, sewage treatment and river engineering. However, it was always recognized that some facets of these would not be able to be dealt with in a national document.

The limitation to civil engineering works meant that major building works, often necessary on contracts for water and sewage treatment works, were not to be covered and this fitted well with the ICE Conditions-based approach that the working group had developed for the new specification. Also, since the Specification for a dam (whether earth, rock or concrete) will inevitably be a specialist and bespoke document, as will much of those for a sea outfall or coastal flood alleviation works, it was inappropriate to consider these types of works. Although commonly found on water services contracts, piling was excluded from the new specification because in 1978 ICE published[16] a national specification and model procedures for this kind of work.

There was one type of civil engineering work that, although highly specialist in nature, it was eventually decided should be included in the new specification. With the advent of the reorganized water industry in 1974 the Well Drillers' Association (WDA) had made strenuous efforts to secure the adoption of its own specification on well drilling contracts. The NWC was reluctant to endorse the trade association's specification but, after reference to the Directors of Operations' Group, it was decided that an appropriate compromise would be for the working group to draft a Section covering *"Wells and boreholes"*, for inclusion in the new specification. *"Boreholes"* would apply to water abstraction works and not to boreholes for ground investigation.

It has to be said that the compromise solution did not sit happily in the new specification. So much so that it was later deleted and published as a Supplement[17], following discussions with representatives of the WDA. Although published in 1985, the Supplement has never been updated.

Even when the working group had identified the aspects of water services civil engineering work that needed to be specified in the new specification, there were still many instances where it was considered that a particular type of work, or a particular material, was too specialist to be dealt with in a national document. Although very subjective, the way the group dealt with these was to consider whether they were the "norm" - could one reasonably expect to find such work, or such materials, on sites throughout England and Wales? If the answer was "yes", then the group set about drafting the necessary clauses; if not, then it was left to those preparing documents for tenderers to draft ad hoc Supplementary Clauses.

For some reason the "norm" yardstick was misunderstood in certain quarters, not least in relation to the various materials specified. Some people went so far as to claim that, if a particular material was not specified in the national specification, then it was banned ! This was especially relevant to newly-developed products and so it was eventually thought appropriate to issue[18] the following clarification:

> *"A requirement of the Specification is that materials used in the Works should comply with any relevant British Standard and that, wherever possible, the Kitemark scheme should also be applied (Clause 2.1). This is a general provision intended for the normal run of established manufactured goods, but it has apparently been the cause of uncertainty in the case of a few newly-developed products for which no British Standard is yet available. Some Engineers appear to have vetoed these on the grounds that, having no British Standard, they do not comply with the Specification.*

The purpose in publishing the specification in this form was to support the use of British Standards, but it was never intended that the document should be used to restrict innovation. In considering the acceptability of new products, therefore, Engineers should be prepared to exercise their right to add appropriate clauses to the specification and, in doing so, should have regard to the Information and Guidance Notes issued from time to time by the NWC/DoE Standing Technical Committee on Sewers and Water Mains and other guidance published by the National Water Council."

The above advice still holds good, despite some of the detail having been overtaken by subsequent events - see Chapters 8 and 9.

The final "scope" issue that the working group had to consider related not to the content of the new specification, but to that which was to comprise individual contracts. No contract would require every clause in the new specification, but should those preparing documents for tenderers by required to identify the clauses to be included, or those to be excluded? It was decided that this issue could be covered by the following omnibus requirement, to be situated along with the disclaimer about guidance.

"Any clauses in this specification which relate to work or materials not required by the Works shall be deemed not to apply."

It will be appreciated that the above words were designed not only to be relevant at Tender stage, but also during the currency of the Contract, when the Engineer may find it necessary to invoke additional clauses as part of an ordered variation to the Works.

7 - CODES

Clause 13(2) of the ICE Conditions requires that *"the mode manner and speed of construction of the Works are to be of a kind and conducted in a manner acceptable to the Engineer"*. More specifically, as regards the actual methods of construction which the Contractor proposes to adopt, Clause 14(6) goes on to provide that:

> *"If requested by the Engineer the Contractor shall submit at such times and in such further detail as the Engineer may reasonably require information pertaining to the methods of construction (including Temporary Works and the use of Contractor's Equipment) which the Contractor proposes to adopt or use and calculations of stresses strains and deflections that will arise in the Permanent Works or any parts thereof during construction so as to enable the Engineer to decide whether if these methods are adhered to the Works can be constructed and completed in accordance with the Contract and without detriment to the Permanent Works when completed."*

A purist might argue, therefore, that the Engineer has all the powers he needs to control the Contractor's method of working and that workmanship, especially Temporary Works, has no place in a performance specification. The working group felt that this was a radical step too far and opted for a slightly more pragmatic approach to workmanship.

It was fundamental that the Specification did not prescribe the specific way in which a particular aspect of the Works was to be constructed, that being a matter for the Contractor. However, it was accepted that there could be reference in the new document to a nationally agreed framework of good practice, where such a framework existed, but exactly where the reference was to be made depended on the nature of the work involved. British Standard codes of practice were an obvious source for such frameworks, especially since they could be relied upon to have been drafted by a committee that included general or specialist contractors' trade associations. The working group drew a distinction between codes of practice which, in the main, comprised standards of good workmanship and those which dealt largely with matters such as Temporary Works. The former were called up as appropriate in the main text of the specification, while the latter, being the Contractor's responsibility under Clause 8(2) of the ICE Conditions, were relegated to the Notes for Guidance.

It had been decided at the outset that the new specification should be written primarily in terms of the performance required, leaving the Contractor, so far as possible, free to decide his method of working. A requirement that the workmanship on a specific aspect of the Permanent Works should be within a nationally agreed framework of good practice was not seen as flying in the face of this approach.

Once the criteria for referring to relevant British Standard codes of practice had been established, it was possible to extend the approach to include other forms of nationally accepted practice. For example, where a contractor was being required to carry out work associated with potable water, or within a sewer or at a sewage works, it is reasonable to expect him to follow the same procedures as recommended for the water industry's own employees.

In each case where a national code of practice existed and was pertinent to the specification, the working group had to decide whether it should be called up in the specification or simply referred to in the Notes for Guidance. These are dealt with in Chapter 12.

26

8 - CERTIFICATION

When the working group began to draft the new specification there were three forms of "certification" that could be prescribed for materials to be used in the Permanent Works. These were:

1. First party certification - whereby the manufacturer alone certified that a product conformed to a particular specification. This was also referred to as "self-certification" and marking a product with a British Standard number in the absence of any other assessment represented such a claim of conformity.

2. Second party certification - whereby certification of conformity to a particular specification was carried out by the purchaser or his agent. This was often used where materials were to be installed in a high risk situation, such as a British Gas pipeline.

3. Third party certification - whereby a body independent of both the manufacturer and the purchaser certified conformity, the best known exponent of this in the United Kingdom being the British Standards Institution (BSI), via its Certification Trade Mark, the "Kitemark".

The working group took the view that first party certification was inadequate for many of the materials used on water services contracts in England and Wales - especially where assets were to buried out of sight and the social and financial consequences of any subsequent failure within a reasonable working life would be severe. Equally, it was not necessary to institute universal second party certification, because almost all of the more important materials had for many years been available with third party certification via the Kitemark. With the approval of the Directors of Operations' Group, the new specification therefore demanded Kitemarked products wherever they were available, though in the light of developments in Europe it subsequently became necessary to modify this a little, for the reasons described in Chapter Nine.

The working group was well aware that if there happened to be only one Kitemark licensee for a particular material the new specification would, in effect, be prescribing a sole supplier, though of course not by name. Faced with this situation, those responsible for some other national specifications inserted a provision whereby there must be at least a certain number of licensees before their demand for third party certification would bite. The group saw this as not only counter to the *raison d'être* for demanding third party certified products, but also as penalising the manufacturer who had gone to the trouble and expense of securing a licence. Several non-licensees who complained were told that the remedy was simple - obtain third party certification ! And over the next few years this many of them did.

In the event that a single Kitemark licensee was unable to supply a particular material when required by the Contractor, the working group relied on Clause 51(1) of the ICE Conditions, by which the Engineer has power to order any variation that he considers to be necessary for the completion of the Works.

In July 1982 the Department of Trade and Industry (DTI) issued a White Paper[19] on *"Standards quality and international competitiveness"* and invited comments from interested parties. The NWC's response[20] was prepared in consultation with the working group and included the following:

> *"The water industry is fully committed to support BSI certification schemes and as part of this commitment is trying to ensure that standards are suitable for the purpose and include the necessary tests etc."*

This commitment to third party certified materials was reinforced in another and rather unusual way in the specification document. A common practice is for contractors' estimators to photostat the relevant page of a proposed specification and then send it to a prospective supplier for a quotation to be used in the preparation of a tender. If an individual clause does not contain a requirement that quality assured products are to be supplied, a supplier can claim no knowledge of such a requirement if a subsequent supply contract is based only on the original photostat.

The practice is not unknown and so it was decided that each page of the Section of the specification dealing with materials should have a bold black stripe down the outside edge of the page, in which attention would be drawn to the fact that quality assured materials were preferred.

For decades it was a prerequisite that a Kitemark licence could only be granted against a British Standard product specification and this policy became an obstacle as the new WIs documents began to appear. Therefore, on 6 November 1985 the WAA Chief Executives' Group agreed to a recommendation[21] that a small "Quality Assurance Working Group" (QAWG) should be set up to explore the possibility of establishing the water industry's own certification scheme.

After appropriate consultations, BSI Quality Assurance in particular, the QAWG concluded[22] that there was a need for a Water Industry Certification Scheme (WICS), to be recognized by the National Accreditation Council for Certification Bodies (NACCB) and to operate in parallel with BSI's certification schemes; indeed, BSI might well be contracted to undertake many of the inspection visits. Whereas BSI would continue to grant a Kitemark licence against a British Standard product specification, WICS would complement this by issuing a "Watermark" licence against a WIs. The final report also included the following vitally important qualification:

> "Participation by manufacturers would be voluntary, as in the case of
> Kitemark schemes. Consequently, participants would need assurance
> that evaluated and quality assured products would receive the
> support from the industry presently enjoyed by Kitemarked goods."

The proposals, including the above qualification, were accepted[23] by the WAA Chief Executives' Group in December 1986 and subsequently endorsed by the WAA Council, comprising the Chairmen of the then water authorities. Although WICS was established during the latter part of 1987 it was not actually launched until 11 October 1988, the first Watermark licence being issued on 22 March 1989.

From that time, it was fondly imagined that not only could the Kitemark be demanded where a BSI Kitemark Certification scheme was available in relation to a British Standard product specification, but also that a WICS Watermark could be required where one was available relative to a WIs. However, it transpired that events in Europe were to have a significant impact on the perceived freedom to specify and, coincidentally, one of the most significant was to occur only a matter of days before the launch of WICS.

In May 1994 all of WICS services were transferred to BSI. WICS marks will be retained for a period of at least two years but BSI will now also be able to offer the Kitemark for product certification and the Registered Firm symbol for quality systems registration.

9 - EUROPE

Water services construction projects are not immune to the various obligations that flow from the United Kingdom's membership of the European Union. The main thrust is via Council Directives, but Judgements of the European Court can have a significant impact.

THE IRISH CASE

At a routine tender meeting in Ireland on 24 June 1986 a decision was made on behalf of Dundalk Urban District Council[24] that was to have profound repercussions for those writing contract Specifications in the European Union.

The council was promoting a scheme for the augmentation of Dundalk's drinking water supply and had engaged a firm of consulting engineers in that connection. One of the associated contracts was for the construction of a pipeline to transport raw water from a river source to a treatment plant and thence into the town's existing distribution system. Clause 4.29 of the proposed contract Specification included the following paragraph:

> *"Asbestos-cement pressure pipes shall be certified as complying with Irish Standard Specification 188: 1975 in accordance with the Irish Standard Mark Licensing Scheme of the Institute for Industrial Research and Standards. All asbestos-cement water mains are to have a bituminous coating internally and externally. Such coatings shall be applied at the factory by dipping."*

One of the tenderers offered a very competitive alternative, whereby the asbestos-cement pipes would conform to ISO 160[25] and be obtained from a Spanish manufacturer. The minutes of the meeting held with the consulting engineer on 24 June 1986 to discuss the tender made it clear that not only was it rejected on the grounds that *"the proposed pipes were not in conformity with Clause 4.29 of the Specification"*, but also that the alternative pipes *"were not examined at that stage"*.

Following a complaint by the contractor whose alternative tender had been rejected, the Commision lodged an application at the European Court on 13 February 1987, supported by Spain, which alleged that a barrier to free trade between Member States had been created, contrary to Article 30 of the EEC Treaty. As is the nature of these things, the Defendent was Ireland, not Dundalk Urban District Council.

The case was heard on 27 April 1988 and in a Judgement[26] on 22 September the European Court declared that:

> *"By allowing the inclusion in the contract Specification for a tender for a public works contract of a clause stipulating that the asbestos cement pressure pipes must be certified as complying with Irish Standard 188: 1975 in accordance with the Irish Standard Mark Licensing Scheme of the Institute for Industrial Research and Standards, Ireland has failed to fulfil its obligations under Article 30 of the EEC Treaty."*

From the standpoint of those writing future contract Specifications in the European Union the Judgement was not entirely a negative one, for it included the following statement:

> *"By incorporating..........the words 'or equivalent' after the reference to the Irish standard..........the Irish authorities could have verified*

> compliance with the technical conditions without from the outset restricting the contract only to tenderers proposing to utilize Irish materials."

Clearly, the working group had to take account of the Judgement. However, rather than add the words *"or equivalent"* after every reference to a British or other standard in the specification, it was decided to insert a general omnibus requirement, making it clear that:

> *"Any reference in the Contract to a Standard published by the British Standards Institution, or to the specification of another body, shall be construed equally as reference to an equivalent one."*

The above device had the additional benefit of providing protection for those drafting ad hoc Supplementary Clauses, but the working group was concerned that one area might still be exposed.

Chapter 8 described how a policy was developed whereby Kitemarked materials were demanded wherever a BSI certification scheme was available in relation to a British Standard product specification, also where WICS had licensed the use of the Watermark in relation to a WIs. It was clear from the Judgement that one aspect of the issues before the Court had been the insistence on pipes bearing the Irish Standard Mark, certifying conformity with Irish Standard 188: 1975. The working group felt, therefore, that it would be safer if equivalence in relation to third party certification was also provided.

THE CONSTRUCTION PRODUCTS DIRECTIVE

The Construction Products Directive[27] (CPD) was adopted on 21 December 1988 and the United Kingdom was one of the first Member States to transpose its provisions into national law, the associated Regulations[28] coming into force on 27 December 1991. One of the Directive's most significant provisions is Article 6, paragraph 1 of which reads as follows:

> *"Member States shall not impede the free movement, placing on the market or use in their territory of products which satisfy the provisions of this Directive.*
>
> *Member States shall ensure that the use of such products, for the purpose for which they were intended, shall not be impeded by rules or conditions imposed by public bodies or private bodies acting as a public undertaking or acting as a public body on the basis of a monopoly position."*

By the time the UK Regulations came into force the water authorities of England and Wales had been privatised, but legal advice to the working group confirmed that, nevertheless, Article 6 had to be observed by a national specification incorporated by reference into individual water services works contracts. However, it is important to appreciate that the Article only relates to *"products which satisfy the provisions of this Directive"*.

Some of the CPD's main provisions relate to the use of *"harmonized standards"*, to be drawn up by the European standards-making bodies, CEN[29] and CENELEC[30], on the basis of mandates given by the Commission. The standards are required to be expressed as far as practicable in product performance terms, having regard to the *"interpretative documents"*. In the words of the CPD these documents[31] *"give concrete form"* to a series of *"essential requirements"* set out in Annex to the Directive.

The members of CEN and CENELEC comprise the national standards-making bodies in countries that are members of the European Union or EFTA. Under the CEN/CENELEC Internal Regulations[32] each member must publish harmonized European standards within a prescribed time of them being available, simultaneously withdrawing its own corresponding national standards. The working group's omnibus equivalence clause was designed to provide comfort each time this occurs; for example, if BS 0000 is withdrawn and replaced by BS EN 9999, the latter is by definition equivalent to the former, whose reference in the specification is effectivelty superseded. The Regulations also stipulate that, whilst a particular harmonized standard is being prepared, new, revised or amended national standards may not normally be issued; this is known as "Standstill".

When describing first, second and third party certification in Chapter 8, care was taken to point out that these were the terms in use when the working group first began work. The CPD does not envisage second party certification and the phrase *"declaration of conformity of the product by the manufacturer"* is used in lieu of first party certification. Therefore, when referring generally to levels of severity, the CPD uses the term *"attestation"*.

The CPD prescribes four systems of conformity attestation, which are summarized in the following table, with descending levels of severity (reading from left to right) depending on the significance of the tasks to be carried out by an approved certification body.

Task	Task performed by			
Conformity of product	ACB	M	M	M
Initial type testing	ACB	M	ACB	M
Factory production control	ACB	ACB	M	M
Key: ACB = Approved certification body M = Manufacturer				

The decision as to which of the four procedures is to apply to a particular product, or class of product, is reserved to the Commission. Such decisions are to be made after appropriate consultations, but the CPD requires that: *"In each case, the least onerous possible procedure consistent with safety shall be chosen"*. It is stressed, however, that all of the four procedures demand factory production control, though not necessarily in accordance with the provisions of EN 29000 (*"Quality systems"*), which is identical in every detail with BS 5750 and ISO 9000. The same cannot be said of many British Standard product specifications and so, in some cases where third party certification is currently not available, the situation from the user's perspective will actually improve.

Nevertheless, there will inevitably be instances where the Commission decides on one of the three levels of attestation that are less stringent than full third party certification and so, in order to comply with the requirement in Article 6(1) described above, the working group had to devise wording that did not fly in the face of such a decision.

Attention was drawn earlier to the fact that the CPD requires harmonized European standards (ENs) to be produced under mandates given by the Commission to CEN/CENELEC, having regard to the *"essential requirements"*. Thus the "mandated" content of a product standard will cover such things as *"terminology"*, *"performance criteria"* and *"methods of test"*, but It is highly probable that many ENs will include provisions that are not covered by the mandates, because such provisions are not considered relevant for the purposes of the CPD. Typical examples would be *"appearance"*, *"geometrical properties"* and (where relative to non-essential requirements) *"performance"*. Any requirements that are not covered by a CPD mandate will be clearly shown in each EN.

The working group resolved to stand by the long-standing commitment to full third party certification as far as possible and so the wording of the specification provides for "automatic" provisions, depending on the circumstances. These can be summarized most easily by the following flow chart:

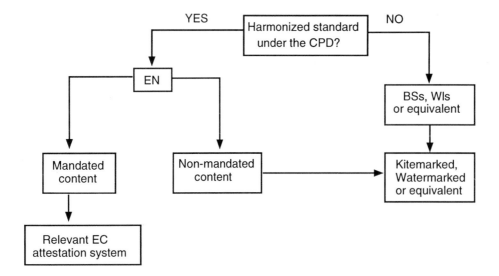

Of course, demanding third party certification for only some of the provisions of a harmonized EN, in circumstances where the Commission has specified a less stringent level of attestation for the rest, may cause problems. Only time will tell.

It is important to stress that the level of attestation decided by the Commission is merely that which is needed to support the use of a "CE" mark under the CPD. The mark signifies that a product meets the requirements of the relevant technical specification (and thereby the essential requirements) and must be allowed free movement throughout the European Union when used for the purpose for which it was intended.

It may be that some manufacturers, perhaps following decisions taken in their respective trade associations, will decide to continue to offer third party certified products, even where representations to the Commission for that level of attestation to apply have proved unsuccessful. By the very nature of the CPD that would not prevent a competitor from selling products also bearing the "CE" mark, but having been subjected to a less stringent level of attestation. If the third party certified products were cheaper, then the purchaser would find no problem in accepting them; if not, he would be obliged to take into account the provisions of Article 6(1) described above.

THE UTILITIES DIRECTIVE

The Utilities Directive[33] was adopted on 17 September 1990 and applies to water services works contracts above prescribed thresholds of estimated value, depending on particular circumstances. The Directive applies to *"the procurement procedures of entities operating in the water, energy, transport and telecommunications sectors"* and was transposed into United Kingdom law by Regulations[34] that came into force on 13 January 1993.

Article 13(2) of the Directive requires that:

> *"technical specifications shall be defined by reference to European specifications where these exist".*

However, Article 13(3) goes on to provide that:

> *"Contracting entities shall define such further requirements as are necessary to complement European specifications or other standards."*

Article 1(7) defines "technical specifications" and states that:

> *"These technical prescriptions may include.............requirements applicable to the material, product, or supply as regards quality assurance..............".*

Accordingly, it has been suggested that, when awarding a contract subject to the provisions of the Utilities Directive, a *"contracting entity"* could invoke the above power and prescribe full third party certification in circumstances where the Commission had specified a lower level of attestation under the CPD. However, the working group's attention was drawn to the fact that Article 13(4) allows only *"such further requirements as are necessary to complement European specifications"* and that the Oxford Dictionary defines *"complement"* in a way which is not synonymous with *"override"*.

The apparently conflicting situations under the two Directives will no doubt be clarified in due course, perhaps even by the repeal of Article 6(1) of the CPD, but legal advice to the working group was that a national specification, being a *"rule or condition"* for the purposes of the CPD, had to err on the side of caution. There is an argument that, relative to an individual contract, the Utilities Directive may allow a contracting entity to "override" an attestation level specified by the Commission under the CPD, but anyone proposing to do so under the present state of knowledge would be well advised to seek expert legal opinion which, at the end of day, is simply that.

10 - STYLE

The preceding chapters have sketched in the background against which the working group put together the national specification, but it is perhaps appropriate to fill in a little more of the detail. As with any standard specification, those preparing documents for tenderers will always have to draft Supplementary Specification Clauses for use with individual contracts and if these follow the same style and philosophy, so much the better.

FORMAT

By definition, every standard specification becomes more and more out of date from the time it is published. Indeed, given the time which must inevitably elapse between finalization and actual publication, it is highly likely that such a specification will in some way have been overtaken by events before the latter takes place.

In order to deal with this the publishers of some national specifications have issued them in loose-leaf form, thereafter issuing amended pages or amendment sheets. At the time the working group was pondering what format to adopt a famous photograph appeared in a technical magazine, showing a pair of scales. On one scale was a well known national specification; on the other, somewhat lower, were the amendments issued since the specification had been published !

Given the many thousands of copies of the new specification that would have to be kept up to date, the working group therefore set its face against the loose-leaf form. Also, in view of the decision to incorporate Notes for Guidance in a wide margin at the left-hand side of the page, it was further decided to opt for an A4 size of document. A means would be found for dealing with any vitally important amendments, but routine things such as changes in connection with British Standards would be left to be picked up by those preparing documents for tenderers. In order to provide for the maximum amount of feedback, the group also decided that the specification would include an invitation for those using it to submit any suggestions for amendment.

ADVISORY NOTES

In the fullness of time it did indeed become necessary to issue vital amendments, though the working group was relieved to find that this was not due to any significant deficiencies in its work ! It was agreed that a system of "Advisory Notes" should be established, the trigger being some issue which, in the opinion of the working group, warranted appropriate advice. Once a decision to prepare an Advisory Note had been taken and endorsed, it would be sensible also to include any amendments that flowed from routine changes which had taken place in other national documents. Again, the obvious examples relate to British Standards.

Because of the fears that any subsequent publication would not reach all those who had acquired copies of the specification (sadly, fears which were later proved to be justified), each Advisory Note emphasized that it was up to those preparing documents for tenderers to follow the advice which it contained. In other words, the original national specification was not amended by any subsequent Advisory Note.

BRITISH STANDARDS

In order to minimize the number of subsequent amendments to the original specification, the working group decided that any reference to a British Standard would cite only its number, not the date. Of course, those preparing documents for tenderers would still have to keep an eye out for changed editions, because of possible implications for a particular contract, but so long as the number remained the same, the reference in the specification would still be valid. As explained in Chapter 9, the advent of the "equivalence" clause meant that even the changing of a number did not, in a contractual sense, require corrective action.

The majority of references in the specification to British Standards are to product specifications but, for the reasons given in Chapter 7, a good many are also to codes of practice. The traditional way of calling up a product specification is to demand that a particular material shall *"comply with the requirements of BS 0000"*, but the working group saw two problems with this. Most product standards include classes, gradings and other options for the purchaser to choose, in which case (so the working group reasoned) the product actually specified would not comply with <u>all</u> of the requirements in the standard - just those specified. Therefore, it was decided that the word *"relevant"* was needed immediately before *"requirements"*.

The second problem was that British Standard codes of practice are written on the basis of recommendations for good, accepted practice. They do not include *"requirements"* and, having decided that it was proper to call up certain codes of practice in connection with workmanship, leaving the Contractor to choose his actual method of working, it was necessary to use a different word. The one chosen was *"provisions"*, which it was felt could be applied equally to product specifications. Therefore, the standard phrase adopted was, and remains, *"shall comply with the relevant provisions of BS 0000"*.

This standard phrase could eventually change if current BSI policy remains and is used as the model. It is clear that BSI sees no need to include the word "relevant" when citing a British Standard, presumably on the grounds that a discrete specification is given by the purchaser when selecting from options within a product standard. By the same token, a contractor deciding upon a particular method from a framework of accepted good practice could be said to have opted for a discrete specification.

The other aspect on which BSI policy might eventually impinge concerns the use of the word *"comply"*. Clause 17.3.4 of BS 0: Part 3[35] reads as follows:

> *"The expressions 'complies with' and 'conforms to' are not quite synonymous. For clarity and consistency of usage conformity should be treated as the attribute of a product, material, process, service or system resulting from compliance by a person or body with a standard or its requirements."*

On this basis, a future edition of the specification would require materials to *"conform to BS 0000"* and, relative to codes of practice, a contractor to *"comply with BS 9999"*!

DRAFTING

Armed with the above, and all the time keeping in mind the DAME rule, those preparing documents for tenderers ought to produce Supplementary Clauses that are a reflection of the main specification's style. Sadly, this is not always the case, as can be seen from many of the suggestions received when comments have been invited in advance of a new edition of the specification. It would be inappropriate to quote an example from these so, by way of illustration of what not to do and why, the following Specification clause for bricks to be used in manholes and culverts was written during the mid 1960's by a young and inexperienced engineer in Leeds.

> *"Clay bricks [shall be of two qualities, shall be used as indicated on the Drawings, in the Specification,][a] [or as directed by the Engineer and][b] shall comply [in all respects][c] with the relevant requirements of BS 3921 [: 1965, 'Clay Engineering Bricks'.][c]*

[Class A bricks shall be used for the inverts to manholes, other parts of structures in direct contact with sewage and the inner ring of brick sewers; Class B bricks shall be used for all other work.]^a

[All bricks shall be obtained from the Accrington Brick and Tile Co.,]^c [or other approved source of similar bricks, (ie one supplier for all grades and types of brick).]^d

[All bricks shall be pressed, hard, sound, regular in form, free from lime, chalk, shells and pebbles,]^e [have flat sides (ie made with little or no indentation or frog)]^a [and be of uniform size, clean, well burnt, with sharp arrises, without cracks and of uniform colour.]^e

[The bricks shall not be twisted or otherwise irregular in shape and shall not bear the maker's name or other distinguishing mark so placed as to be visible when the bricks have been laid in work.]^e

[When brought to the Site the bricks shall be unloaded by hand and carefully stacked for use.]^f [Any damaged bricks, bats, old bricks or any bricks that may be rejected by the Engineer shall be immediately broken up or removed from the Site.]^g

[Samples of bricks delivered to the Site shall be taken at random from a load and deposited with, and approved by, the Engineer before any of the load shall be used in the Works. All subsequent deliveries of bricks shall be generally up to the standard of the sample.]^d

[Bricks submitted for sample shall be retained for reference during the period of the Contract, in the office of the Engineer or his Representative.]^c

[All testing of bricks shall be carried out in accordance with BS 3921: 1965.]^e

The key to the various references against phrases in square brackets is as follows:

> a = see CESMM, class K, additional description rule A1;
> b = see Sixth Edition, Clause 13(1);
> c = redundant;
> d = see Sixth Edition, Clauses 13(2) and 36(1);
> e = see BS 3921;
> f = not product specification; and
> g = see Sixth Edition, Clause 39(1).

The somewhat dramatic outcome of applying the DAME rule to the above is, therefore:

> *"Clay bricks shall comply with the relevant requirements of BS 3921."*

INCORPORATION OF SPECIFICATION INTO CONTRACTS

A Guidance Note[36] issued in 1977 by the CCSJC included the following advice relative to the use of the ICE Conditions:

> *"It is not normally necessary to bind copies of the ICE Conditions of Contract into the documents prepared for tenderers although if the ICE Conditions are not bound in it will be necessary to provide in the*

tender documents a copy of the Form of Tender and Appendix to the Form of Tender.

Whether or not the ICE Conditions are bound in the following should appear in the documents of the Contract:

'The Conditions of Contract are Clauses 1 to 71 inclusive of the Conditions of Contract and Forms of Tender, Agreement and Bond for use in connection with Works of Civil Engineering Construction, Fifth Edition (June 1973) approved by the Institution of Civil Engineers, the Association of Consulting Engineers and the Federation of Civil Engineering Contractors and commonly known as the ICE Conditions of Contract together with the following special conditions:

Special conditions

72. The following special conditions form part of the Conditions of Contract. 73. etc.

The administration of Contracts is facilitated if the ICE Conditions of Contract are bound into copies of the Contract documents provided for the use of those directly involved in the administration of the Contract."

The working group saw this sound advice as a good model for using the new specification and drafted appropriate guidance for inclusion in an appendix at the rear of the document. This prompted a discussion on what the new specification should be called and initially the group opted for *"Civil Engineering Specification for Water Authority Works"*. However, in deference to the part played by the WCA in its preparation, and bearing in mind that the NWC's logo on the cover would automatically link it to England and Wales, this was later changed to the *"Civil Engineering Specification for the Water Industry"*. It was perhaps inevitable that such a mouthful should become widely known as *"CESWI"*.

11 - EVOLUTION

Much has happened since that day in April 1974 when the NWC Directors of Operations' Group decided that there should be a common specification for water services civil engineering contracts in England and Wales. The working group's first composite draft has evolved through successive published editions, supplemented by Advisory Notes at important times, and it is interesting to note the major issues that have led to the various stages in CESWI's evolution.

DRAFT FOR PUBLIC COMMENT

The first composite draft[37] was issued by the NWC for public comment in March 1977 and contained the following sections:

    1 - General
    2 - Materials
    3 - Excavation, backfilling and restoration
    4 - Formwork and concrete
    5 - Construction of pipelines and tunnels
    6 - Manholes, chambers and brickwork
    7 - Testing and sterilization
    8 - Well boring
    9 - Roadworks

In addition to the ten water authorities, local authorities that carried out sewerage functions on their behalf, the WCA and the STCSWM, copies of the draft were also sent to seven Government departments, four local authority associations, 13 professional bodies, six contractors' trade associations and 13 manufacturers' trade associations. A period of two months was allowed for comment and it was pleasing to note that the great majority of those invited to comment took the time and trouble to do so. The working group then set about the task of considering each of the many hundreds of suggestions.

CESWI

The first edition[38] of CESWI was published by the NWC in July 1978 and, apart from minor changes in terminology, had the same eight sections as the draft for comment.

CESWI - ADVISORY NOTE NO.1

Prevention of contamination of water supplies is vital and the original edition of CESWI required that, where the Contractor was engaged on work associated with potable water supplies, he had to comply with the provisions of *"Safeguards to be adopted in the operation and management of waterworks"*, which had been issued by the Ministry of Housing and the Welsh Office in 1967. This was superseded in January 1979 when the NWC published *"Water supply hygiene - Safeguards in the operation and management of public waterworks in England and Wales"*.

Safe working in sewers and at sewage works is no less important and, when doing so, the original specification had required the Contractor to conform to *"Safety in sewers and at sewage works"*, the last edition of which was published by ICE in 1969 because, in July 1979, the National Joint Health and Safety Committee for the Water Service (NJHSCWS) published its *"Health and safety guideline No. 2 - Safe working in sewers and at sewage works"*.

The first Advisory Note to CESWI[39] was therefore published in October 1980 and advised those preparing documents for tenderers to note the publication of these two important new codes, along with several other changes that had recently occurred relative to British Standards. Notable among these had been the publication of BS 5607[40] - the code of practice for safe use of explosives in the construction industry.

CESWI - ADVISORY NOTE NO.2

Reference was made in Chapter 6 to the fact that misunderstandings had begun to be reported as to the standing of newly-developed products relative to CESWI. So much so that the working group felt it important to issue clarification by way of a second Advisory Note[41] and this was published in October 1981. Once again the opportunity was taken to advise those preparing tender documents of recent changes in connection with British Standards.

CESWI-2

With the benefit of four years' successful experience with the first edition of CESWI it was decided to prepare a second one, though this time WRc would provide the working group with a Technical Secretary and publish the new document. Perhaps the easiest way to describe the more important differences between the original and new documents is to quote the Foreword to CESWI-2[42]:

> *"The Civil Engineering Specification for the Water Industry was first published by the National Water Council in July 1978 and since then it is estimated that the document has been used on more than 4,000 contracts in England and Wales worth over £1,000m.*

> *A preliminary survey carried out by the Water Research Centre in April 1982 showed that sufficient experience had been gained to warrant a review of the specification to be followed by publication of a second edition. This present document is the result of that review.*

> *Comments were invited from within the industry and from manufacturers, professional institutions and from other interested parties. In total some 55 organizations submitted comments.*

> *The changes made have been of two kinds - first, updating of factual references such as British Standard numbers and second, revision or expansion of certain clauses where experience has shown this to be desirable. Most amendments in the latter category are of a minor nature but two important changes have been made involving complete Sections of the document. In the first edition Section 8 covered Wells and Boreholes. Comments from users conveyed a general feeling that this was too specialist a subject for a general specification and one which would be better dealt with by means of a separate supplementary document. The original Section 8 has therefore been removed together with relevant clauses from other sections. Conversely, although the first edition did not cover building works, many users have commented that such coverage would be useful since many of the water industry's civil engineering contracts include relatively simple buildings.*

> *Section 6 has therefore been completely restructured and extended to deal with building works and the balance of clauses from the old Section 6 on manholes, etc., transferred to Section 5 which has been*

retitled. Two further significant additions have been the extensions of Section 3 to cover reinstatement of highway trenches, and of Section 4 to cover structures designed to retain aqueous liquids. The former has been made possible by progressively increased adoption of the PUSWA Conference Model Agreement and Specification, the new clauses closely following that specification document and having been drafted in consultation with a number of highway authorities. Despite these changes the purpose of the specification remains unchanged, namely to cover the types of civil engineering work most commonly undertaken by the water industry.

As with the first edition it is envisaged that it will often be necessary to include additional clauses to provide for individual features and the need for such clauses has been allowed for in the system of numbering. The system should be followed when numbering any additional clauses in order to maintain consistency of presentation."

CESWI-2 was published in July 1984 by WRc on behalf of WAA, the NWC having been dissolved on 30 September 1983 under the provisions of the Water Act 1983[43].

CESWI-2 - ADVISORY NOTE NO.1

In November 1985 ICE published a second edition[44] of CESMM and this prompted the working group to draft an Advisory Note[45] to CESWI-2. Chapter 4 described earlier how CESWI sought to refer only to any "grey" areas of coverage in CESMM as regards water services works and, on reading CESMM2, the group was delighted to find that many of the issues that it had highlighted in the first two editions of CESWI had now been clarified.

The *"Formwork and concrete"* section of CESWI had originally been drafted largely on the basis of recommendations in CP 110 (*"Code of practice for the structural use of concrete"*). However, this was replaced by BS 8110[46] in August 1985 and so, in addition to the usual reporting of changes in British Standards, the Advisory Note gave guidance to those preparing documents for tenderers on the implications for CESWI that flowed from the new code. It was published by WRc on behalf of WAA in August 1986.

CESWI-3

By the summer of 1987 the working group's thoughts had begun to turn towards the preparation of a third edition of CESWI and, having received authority to proceed, it set off into what was by now familiar territory, though this time with several new faces round the table following the retirement of many of the original members. Once again, the changes that were found to be necessary can best be summarized by quoting from the Foreword to the eventual CESWI-3[47], which was once more published by WRc on behalf of WAA, in May 1989:

"In 1987 it was decided to initiate a national survey to elicit comments on how the second edition of the specification might be improved. Announcements were subsequently made in appropriate publications and comments were invited from within the water industry.

The principal changes reflect the publication since 1984 of revised editions of several documents to which reference is made. Notable among these are the British Standard codes of practice for the structural use of concrete and the design of concrete structures for

---

retaining aqueous liquids; also the Department of Transport's (DTp's) specification for highway works[48].

In October 1988 the water industry launched its own certification scheme (WICS), to enable products not covered by a British Standard (and therefore unable to be Kitemarked) to be independently certified by application of the 'Watermark'. Such products are manufactured to water industry specifications used by WICS for the purposes of assessing product conformity. Section 2 of the specification has therefore been extended to reflect the launch of WICS.

Account has been taken of the 1988 European Court of Justice Judgement in the case of the EC versus Ireland, in which it was held that the Treaty of Rome obliged Member States not to preclude consideration of products manufactured to specifications other than their own. The wording of the specification is also consistent with the UK's interpretation of the requirements of the proposed EC Construction Products Directive. In response to many requests a further Section has been added to the specification, covering fundamental requirements for sewer renovation works carried out under the ICE Conditions of Contract. The Section has also been drafted to be compatible with the sewer renovation class of the Civil Engineering Standard Method of Measurement.

Whilst this edition of the specification was in draft, the Water Bill was presented to Parliament. The Bill includes proposals for water and sewerage undertakers to submit to the Secretary of State for approval, codes of practice with respect to the exercise of undertakers' pipe-laying powers. Assuming Parliament approves these proposals, it is likely that such codes of practice will include some matters at present covered in this specification. Accordingly no revisions have been made in this respect to Section 1 of the specification."

The water authorities were duly privatised on 1 September 1989 and it was heartening to note that all of the new water service companies continued to use CESWI. Further, they continued to nominate representatives to the working group, now under the auspices of the Water Services Association (WSA), which had been established as the successor trade association to WAA on 1 September 1989, following the privatisations brought about by the Water Act 1989[49].

CESWI-3 - ADVISORY NOTE NO.1

Chapter 8 described the implications for CESWI and the water industry of the CPD or, to be more precise, the Construction Products Regulations 1991. In preparation for the situation that would exist after the Regulations came into force on 27 December 1991 the working group prepared an Advisory Note[50] for use in connection with CESWI-3.

Much of the groundwork had been done by the inclusion of the omnibus "equivalence" clause in CESWI-3, but those preparing documents for tenderers were advised to note further changes that were considered essential in relation to attestation and quality assurance. Attention was also drawn to the Utilities Directive and the powers that some thought it gave contracting entities as regards levels of attestation (see Chapter 9). Because of the importance of the issue, the Advisory Note was confined to issues that directly related to the CPD. It was published in October 1991.

CESWI-3 - ADVISORY NOTE NO.2

A further significant event that occurred during 1991 was the publication in January of the Sixth Edition of the ICE Conditions of Contract. There was some concern initially that, compared to the Fifth Edition, the balance of risk in the Sixth had tipped towards the Contractor and many of the water service companies shared this view.

Over the next year or so each of the companies, along with the statutory water companies, took stock of the situation until, by May 1992, the working group was able to report[51] to the WSA's Water Services Management Group (WSMG) that *"all of the water service companies and many of the statutory water companies have recently changed, or plan to change, to using the Sixth Edition"*. Authority to prepare a second Advisory Note[52] to CESWI-3, devoted exclusively to the implications of the Sixth Edition, was therefore secured and this was published in June 1992.

CESWI-4

Although a second Advisory Note to CESWI-3 had to be issued in June 1992 to reflect the trend towards using the Sixth Edition, this coincided with the thought that the time was ripe to begin to put together a fourth edition of the specification. Quite apart from the privatisation of the water authorities, a great deal had been happening, or was about to happen, that impacted on CESWI and the more important issues are summed up in the following extract from the Foreword to the subsequent CESWI-4[53]:

> *"The principal changes reflect the transfer of water supply and sewerage functions to water service companies and the coming into force of the New Roads and Street Works Act 1991[54], together with its associated Regulations and Codes of Practice. Also, following the lead set by the Third Edition of the Civil Engineering Standard Method of Measurement[55], the section on sewer renovation has been extended to cover water main renovation and ancillary works. Clauses relating to steel pipelines, omitted since the first edition, have been reintroduced."*

CESWI-4 was published by WRc on behalf of WSA in October 1993.

12 - ANALYSIS

When asked how to interpret a particular document, an eminent water industry lawyer once replied "don't ask me what it means - I wrote it !". The reader is asked to reflect on the full subtlety of that reply before embarking on, or quoting from, the following chapter; and always to remember that the interpretation of a Contract is a matter for the Engineer or, ultimately, an Arbitrator. The following analysis of CESWI-4 is offered on that cautionary note.

No effort has been made to comment on every single clause in the new specification, especially where the Notes for Guidance add all that is necessary, or where a simple updating of a reference is all that has occurred. The commentary is, therefore, limited to useful background information as to why particular wording was developed, and to changes that have been made in the light of comments received on CESWI-3.

PRODUCT SPECIFICATIONS AND LEVELS OF ATTESTATION

The impact of the CPD and the "Irish" Case was described in Chapters 8 and 9, but it is appropriate to draw attention to the following paragraph which has been added to this introductory note, after the reference to newly-developed products:

> *"However, in the case of any innovatory product for which no British Standard or Water Industry specification (or the equivalent of either) exists, preference should be given to products which have been assessed by a third party approvals body as being fit for their intended purpose. Typical UK-based organizations offering such services are the Water Industry Certification Scheme (WICS) and the British Board of Agrément (BBA). The former works closely with the water industry in developing specifications for new products and the latter is authorised to issue European Technical Approvals under the provisions of the Construction Products Directive."*

The paragraph should be read in the context of Chapter 3, in which it was pointed out that CESWI covers the "norm" - could one reasonably expect to find this product on sites throughout England and Wales? In the case of innovatory products the answer is clearly "no" and so it is left to those preparing documents for tenderers, or possibly Engineers if approached to consider ordering a variation, to decide on the suitability of a particular new product.

Knowledge that a material conforms to a specification which is in the public domain and has been agreed by representatives of all interested parties gives comfort to those making decisions as to its possible use, as does the availability of third party certification; such is the case with British Standards and associated Kitemarking. However, the specification for an innovative product may well be commercially sensitive and this presents difficulties for those being asked to consider using the product.

The new paragraph in CESWI-4 advises that *"preference should be given to products which have been assessed by a third party approvals body as being fit for their intended purpose"* and, of course, this means preference over any other innovative material that lacks such assurance, not preference over established materials that, for example, conform to British Standards and bear the Kitemark ! But although third party assurance is comforting, there can still be the problem of the specification against which the approvals body has assessed the material.

Before making any decision relative to an innovatory product, it would be prudent to ask oneself a few pertinent questions. Can I have sight of the specification? If not, have the water service companies been involved in its production? What assurances have I, through the third party approvals body, that the product will perform over a reasonable working life?

None of this is to damn newly-developed products. It is simply that those being asked to consider the use of a particular material have to strike a balance between discouraging innovation and being satisfied, as far as possible, that the material's performance over a reasonable working life will match that of established ones.

Turning to the end of this introductory note, starting with CESWI-2 successive editions have included an invitation to complete and submit a form (given as Appendix XI in CESWI-4) where problems are encountered relative to quality assured products. The procedure cannot affect the provisions of a contract, but it is to the benefit of all concerned if problems are brought to the attention of the certification body.

SECTION 1 - GENERAL

Chapter 11 described how the Foreword to CESWI-3 included the following paragraph:

> "Whilst this edition of the specification was in draft, the Water Bill was presented to Parliament. The Bill includes proposals for water and sewerage undertakers to submit to the Secretary of State for approval, codes of practice with respect to the exercise of undertakers' pipe-laying powers. Assuming Parliament approves these proposals, it is likely that such codes of practice will include some matters at present covered in this specification. Accordingly no revisions have been made in this respect to Section 1 of the specification."

The DoE elected to draft a model code of practice and consulted the water industry during its preparation. Therefore, it was possible to align many of the model code's provisions with those of CESWI and so avoid wholesale amendments to the specification - especially the General Clauses. The model code[56] was sent to WAA in July 1989 as the basis for water and sewerage undertakers drafting their own codes for submission for the Secretary of State's approval.

1.1   ENTRY ONTO THE SITE

Much of this clause complements Clauses 41 and 42 of the Sixth Edition, in that it recognizes that the Employer has responsibilities to owners and any occupiers and may have made prior arrangements with them. Like many of the other General Clauses, the aim is to formalize accepted good practice. Note that the phrase "commencement of operations" is used, rather than *"Works Commencement Date"*, so as to localize the procedures.

Each *"Code of Practice for the Exercise of Works Powers on Land"* is an approved statutory document whose provisions apply to the undertaker, whether or not the works are being executed by a local authority on behalf of a sewerage undertaker under statutory arrangements. Of course, such arrangements recognize this, but in all cases it is necessary to pass on to the Contractor the obligations of the Code that fall to his responsibility in practice. Therefore, a new sub-clause 3 has been added, together with a fourth Note for Guidance.

1.2   SURVEY OF HIGHWAYS, PROPERTIES, LANDS AND CROPS

This is a classic example of the specification's efforts to mirror accepted good practice. It is in everyone's interests if an agreed record can be established before work is commenced.

1.3 SITE FENCING

A Note For Guidance in earlier editions of CESWI pointed out that Part 5(ii) of Chapter 8 of the Traffic Signs Manual[57] dealt with the fencing of obstructions and excavations in highways. This has been deleted because Clause 1.12 requires compliance with the provisions of Chapter 8.

1.5 ACCOMMODATION FOR THE ENGINEER

Over the years there have been repeated calls from some quarters for CESWI to take the lead and standardize office accommodations for the Engineer. The majority view was that this was best left to individual undertakers, but it has now been possible to add an extra Note for Guidance, drawing attention to the fact that BS 6767: Part 1[58] deals with transportable accommodation units.

Sub-clause 1 requires that offices and other accommodations *"shall be erected, furnished, equipped and ready for occupation within 7 days of the Works Commencement Date"*. This was another instance where a sensible balance had to be struck. Several commentators wanted the offices and accommodations to be fully available "before the Works Commencement Date", but that is clearly impossible, since the associated activities are part of the Works ! Others suggested *"before the commencement of the Permanent Works"*, but it is quite possible that the Engineer's Representative will want to watch and supervise significant Temporary Works, especially excavations, being undertaken at the outset of the Contract.

The period of 7 days recognizes that erecting and equipping the offices and accommodations are not only part of the Works, but under the Contractor's direct control. The longer period of 28 days allowed for the installation of services acknowledges that the actual provision of utilities' services to the Contractor's order is outside his control and may very well take longer than 7 days.

1.7 INTERFERENCE WITH LAND INTERESTS

The Water Industry Act 1991[59] imposes duties on water and sewerage undertakers for the protection of the environment and this is highlighted in the revised Note for Guidance (ii).

1.8 INTERFERENCE WITH ACCESS TO PROPERTIES AND APPARATUS

In sub-clause 2 the term *"Public Utility and privately owned"* has been deleted on the grounds that it was redundant. The shortened requirement is quite clear.

1.10 PROTECTION AGAINST DAMAGE

In sub-clause 1 the term *"currency of the Contract"* is used, rather than the more formal *"Time for Completion and the last (if more than one) Defects Correction Period"*.

Just as the CCSJC found it necessary in 1993 to issue a corrigenda sheet[60] to the Sixth Edition to recognize the introduction of the New Roads and Street Works Act 1991, so the working group had to re-examine CESWI-3 in order to take account of the Act's provisions. This is the first clause to reflect the new situation. Formerly, the term *"Public Utility"* had been coined by the group but now, for consistency with the new Act and to reflect the situation as found, it has been replaced in sub-clause 2 by *"Statutory Undertakers, the Highway Authority...."*. Sub-clause 3 also had an undefined and therefore rather meaningless term - *"Statutory Authority"* and this too has been replaced by *"Statutory Undertaker, Highway Authority...."*.

1.11 APPARATUS OF STATUTORY UNDERTAKERS, HIGHWAY AUTHORITIES AND OTHERS

This clause was one of the most difficult to draft when the first edition of the specification was being prepared. After many abortive attempts it was eventually decided simply to try and reflect what most would see as a sequence of accepted good practice and this appears to have stood the test of time. Although the principle has been adhered to, the clause and its heading have undergone major surgery as a result of the New Roads and Street Works Act 1991. It is not necessary here to detail the various instances of revised terminology that flow from the Act, but attention should be drawn to the following significant changes:

1.   Although sub-clause 1 has been rewritten, legal advice was still to the effect that it remains lawful to disclaim the accuracy and completeness of any information about apparatus which may be indicated in the Contract in good faith.

2.   The original sub-clause 4 required the Contractor to *"make his own arrangements for any diversion or removal of services which he may require for his own convenience or because of his proposed method of working"*, but a revised procedure has now been introduced whereby the Contractor notifies the Engineer of any diversions that he may require, so that the Employer can be asked to make the necessary arrangements with the appropriate Statutory Undertaker(s) - see also the revised Note for Guidance (iv); and

3.   Two new Notes for Guidance now advise that *"any requirements of Statutory Undertakers or public bodies should be described in the Contract"* and *"for works likely to affect other apparatus in a street see Section 69 of the New Road and Street Works Act 1991"*.

A small but significant amendment in sub-clause 2 is that the adjective describing the *"programme of Works"* is now *"accepted"*, not *"approved"*. Students of the Sixth Edition will recognize that this reflects Clause 14(2)(a) of that document.

The final change of any significance here is that Note for Guidance (ii) has been updated to quote the 1993 edition[61] of the *"Model Consultative Procedure for Pipeline Construction Involving Deep Excavation"*, though citing the date is inconsistent with how British Standards are quoted. See Chapter 10.

1.12 TRAFFIC REQUIREMENTS

Sub-clause 1 has been completely rewritten in the light of the 1991 Act. Water and sewerage undertakers are now subject to the requirements of the *"Safety at Street Works and Road Works"* code of practice, issued by the Secretary of State under the provisions of the Act, and this obligation is passed on to the Contractor. Although Undertakers are not actually required to comply with Chapter 8 of the Traffic Signs Manual (*"Traffic Safety Measures for Road Works"*), or with DTp advice notes regarding traffic signals, compliance with these is retained, since this has been demanded by successive editions of CESWI.

The term *"traffic"*, in the relevant context, applies equally to pedestrians and this is recognized in the clause. It should also be noted that the proper term *"footway"* and not *"footpath"*, which has entirely different meaning, is used. However, where any of the Works affect a *"public footpath"*, this is covered in sub-clause 4 by the phrase *"public right of way"* so that, for example, bridle-paths are also covered.

Sub-clause 6 provides two good examples of not specifying the impossible. The Contractor cannot prevent his vehicles depositing mud or other debris on roads and footways, but he can *"take all reasonable steps"* to stop this happening. Equally, he cannot wave a magic wand and instantly remove any material that is deposited, but it is reasonable to expect him to do this *"expeditiously"*.

1.14 WORKS AFFECTING WATERCOURSES

The Water Act 1989 did not transfer the water authorities' land drainage functions to the new water service companies, but to the National Rivers Authority (NRA). Therefore, although this clause has not been amended, a new Note for Guidance (ii) has been added, advising those preparing documents for tenderers that *"any requirement for the Contractor to liaise with the appropriate Land Drainage Authority should be detailed in the Contract"*. Of course, such Authorities are not necessarily the NRA, so it could be argued that this advice is long overdue !

The statutory references in what is now Note for Guidance (iii) have been updated to reflect the introduction of the Water Resources Act 1991[62] and the Land Drainage Act 1991[63].

1.15 CONTAMINATION OF WATER SUPPLIES

Chapter 11 described how the NWC's *"Water supply hygiene - Safeguards in the operation and management of public waterworks in England and Wales"* came to be prescribed in the specification. In September 1988 the WAA issued a further version[64] of the document and this is now reflected in the clause and Note for Guidance (i) - a little belatedly, for it was actually published in time to have been called up in CESWI-3 !

Chlorine and sulphur dioxide are often used at waterworks but rarely by the Contractor. Accordingly, the old Clause 1.16 (*"Chlorine and sulphur dioxide"*) has now been deleted.

1.17 WORK IN COMPRESSED AIR

The Work in Compressed Air Special Regulations[65] incorporate decompression tables (known as the "Blackpool tables") which the Contractor is required to follow when working in compressed air. However, the Regulations provide for the Chief Inspector of Factories to approve the use of alternative tables and, since a CIRIA research project had led to a tables based on more recent investigations, the working group decided to take advantage of this provision and require the Contractor to make an application to use them.

The CIRIA code was reprinted with amendments[66] in 1992 and so the clause has been adjusted accordingly. Since the code also gives recommendations on accepted good practice for work in compressed air, attention has been drawn to this in an extra Note for Guidance, consistent with the policy towards codes of practice described in Chapter 7.

1.19 EXPLOSIVES AND DANGEROUS SUBSTANCES

Sub-clause 3 has been extended to recognize the legal situation under which the Contractor operates when storing blasting explosives. In addition to requiring that the provisions of BS 5607[67] are followed, the sub-clause now also requires that storage is in accordance with the conditions (if any) of the relevant statutory licence obtained by the Contractor. Given the DAME rule and the policy for codes of practice, the purist might argue that, rather than being extended, sub-clause 3 might well have been deleted !

1.21 BRITISH STANDARDS AND OTHER DOCUMENTS

Although this clause remains unaltered, the reader's particular attention is drawn to Chapter 9 as regards the importance of sub-clause 2 - the omnibus equivalence clause.

ASSOCIATED TOPICS

Most of the amendments here comprise the updating of statutory references, but the background to Associated Topic 1 ("Noise") should be mentioned. A small minority of the original working group felt that, given the legal situation in which Employers can now find themselves in relation to the control of construction noise, the specification should include appropriate provisions. The majority view is set out in Associated Topic 1.

SECTION 2 - MATERIALS

An early criticism of this Section when CESWI was first published in 1978 was that it was "just a list of British Standards", which was difficult to understand in the context of a standard specification. However, it is possible that that the critics' main cause for concern was that the ten multifunctional water authorities in England and Wales might have been expected to show their muscle and specify more stringent requirements than those in the British Standards that were most relevant to the water industry. This was to misunderstand the industry's post-1974 approach to the drafting of British Standards.

The working group was well aware that in January 1978 the NWC Directors of Operations' Group had given its backing[68] to the policy of securing adequate representation at all levels on BSI committees, in order that the water industry's views could be taken fully into account. Representation in those days was arranged and co-ordinated by the STCSWM.

The Directors of Operations later agreed[69] that the water industry's representatives on BSI committees would be better able to obtain the views of water authorities on draft British Standards if each Director was to nominate a member of his staff to receive such drafts and elicit comments from within his authority. The system of *"Water Industry Standards Liaison Officers"* survives to this day and now includes Standards Liaison Officers representing the WCA and the water industries of Scotland and Northern Ireland. Its importance has increased markedly with the advent of draft European Standards (prENs).

The constitutions of the STCSWM and its sub-committees not only reflected all sides of the water industry, but also associated organizations. Therefore, in a refinement and strengthening of its policy as regards the water authorities' voice at BSI (further shades of *"he who pays the piper....."*), the Directors of Operations' Group agreed[70] in 1980 that it would decide on appointments to BSI committees; also that *"any significant divergence of view on any matter"* should be referred to the Group for decision, not the STCSWM. However, general activity would still be co-ordinated by the STCSWM.

The STCSWM's successor was the SWMC, but after privatisation it was replaced by the UK Water Industry Engineering and Operations Committee, whose membership is more closely tailored to the water industry. Therefore, it was appropriate for the industry's BSI and international standards representation and work, together with the development of any WIs or IGN, to be co-ordinated by that committee, acting through its Materials and Standards Group. The commitment was further strengthened in 1990 when the Group's Chairman, Mr David E. Burgess, was seconded to the WSA to direct and co-ordinate activity.

2.1 STANDARDS AND SUBMISSION OF MATERIALS

The basic requirements of sub-clause 1 as regards levels of attestation were described in Chapter 8, while Chapter 9 explained the impact of the CPD and the "automatic" provisions that apply through sub-clause 3 wherever the Commission has decided on a level lower than full third party certification in relation to a particular product. As regards the certification bodies, it is not lawful to require that they should be accredited by an "equivalent" organization to the NACCB, because not all Member States have such an organization and to do so would, therefore, constitute a barrier to trade. Consequently, the specification provides for an equivalent certification mark.

The references in sub-clause 3 and Note for Guidance (vii) to what might be the provisions of a Directive other than the CPD (such as the Utilities Directive) as regards specifying further quality assurance requirements were dealt with in Chapter 9. The reader is once again cautioned to tread very warily in this connection.

A minor, yet significant, addition has been made to sub-clause 4. In order to recognize the practical situation that might exist at a particular time, successive editions of the specification have provided that

"The requirements of sub-clauses 1 and 2 above as regards third party certification shall not apply where the Engineer is satisfied and confirms to the Contractor in writing that third party quality assured materials are not readily available."

The words *"or appropriate"* have now been added to the end of this sub-clause and could put the Engineer in a rather invidious position. Through the Contract, the Employer has stated his general wish for the provision and use of third party quality assured materials and Clause 51(1) of the Sixth Edition sets out the Engineer's powers for ordering variations as follows:

"The Engineer

(a) shall order any variation to any part of the works that is in his opinion necessary for the completion of the works and

(b) may order any variation that for any other reason shall in his opinion be desirable for the completion and/or improved functioning of the Works."

Depending on the circumstances, either of these powers could be invoked by the Engineer to deal with a situation where third party quality assured materials are not readily available; but what power does the Engineer rely on, given the Employer's expressed wish in the Contract, if he decides that such materials are "not appropriate" ? Perhaps any Employer who is prepared to allow the Engineer to derogate from the blanket requirement for third party certification should have been advised through a Note for Guidance to follow the procedure set out in Clause 2(1)(b) of the Sixth Edition and state the relevant requirements in Item 18 of the Appendix to the Form of Tender.

Note for Guidance (v) is particularly comprehensive and deals with materials which might affect drinking water quality. It has been extended to include the following sentence:

"Before accepting any material which will come into contact with potable water, or water to be used for potable supply, the Engineer shall have regard to the provisions of Regulation 25 of the Water Supply (Water Quality) Regulations 1989[71]".

This is a rather onerous provision and those who find themselves in the position of having to take account of it might benefit from the following thoughts:

1. It is a little strange to see an apparently mandatory requirement in a Note for Guidance;

2. It might have been clearer to say *"....Water Supply (Water Quality) Regulations 1989 as amended"*, because anyone who simply reads Regulation 2(12) will miss the fact that the Water Supply (Water Quality) (Amendment) Regulations[72] inserted the crucial word *"adversely"* after *"affect"*!

3. Regard to the Regulations must not only be had by the Engineer on behalf of the Employer (the "water undertaker") when considering whether a particular material is acceptable, but also by those preparing documents for tenderers; and

4. Regulation 25 does not demand that all materials must appear on a statutorily-approved list, it also provides for the use of ones which the undertaker is satisfied will not have any adverse effect on water quality, or ones that have been used satisfactorily in the past.

2.2 STORAGE OF MATERIALS

This clause is a prime example of the performance approach. Compare it to an example of the kind of hotchpotch that the young engineer in Leeds (not to mention others up and down the country) was writing in the 1960s:

> *"Unless approval is given for the handling of cement in bulk, all cement shall be delivered in sound, properly secured bags and stored in a dry weatherproof shed with a raised wooden floor not less than 6 inches above ground level with a free air space beneath, or other building approved by the Engineer. Cement shall be delivered in quantities sufficient to ensure that there is no suspension or interruption of the work of concreting at any time and each consignment shall be kept separate and distinct. Any cement that shall have become injuriously affected by damp or other causes shall at once be removed from the Site. Cement shall be stored in such a manner that it is used in the same order in which it is delivered."*

The CESWI clause not only avoids the unnecessary references to "method" but, in just two short sentences, the Contractor is made fully aware of what is required as regards the storage of any materials that he uses in connection with the Works.

2.3 HANDLING AND USE OF MATERIALS

This is also an important omnibus clause, picking up on the theme of "accepted good practice". A good example of the type of operation that it covers is the handling of concrete pipes, which are often very heavy. Here again our friend from Leeds was generating a full head of steam all those years ago:

> *"The Contractor shall provide suitable apparatus to the approval of the Engineer for off-loading and handling concrete pipes. Under no circumstances whatsoever will a wire sling be permitted through the pipe barrel and any pipes suffering damage resulting from any means will be immediately rejected from the Site."*

CESWI simply requires that the manufacturer's recommendations are followed, those for concrete pipes being set out in a Concrete Pipe Association (CPA) Technical Bulletin[73].

2.6 GRASS SEED

A common complaint during the time that the first edition of CESWI was being prepared was that grass seed as specified in several national specifications was difficult, if not impossible, to obtain. The working group sought to remedy this by developing an entirely new specification in consultation with seed merchants, the practical background to this being given in the various Notes for Guidance.

2.10 AGGREGATES FOR CONCRETE

Much effort has been devoted to ensuring that this clause and its associated Notes for Guidance follow the latest nationally-accepted documents. This is typified by the way in which alkali-silica reaction has been dealt with, the latest change being the addition of a reference to Clause 4.2.4 of BS 5328: Part 1[74] in Note for Guidance (iii).

A more contentious aspect, at least in some parts of the country, concerns the use of marine aggregates in concrete. The clause requires that aggregates from natural sources must conform to BS 882[75] which, rather than prohibit the use of marine aggregates, imposes limits on shell content and provides for the limitation of chloride ion content. Limits on the chloride ion content of the total concrete mix are specified in Clause 4.9 of CESWI-4. All of these provisions are consistent with the recommendations of BS 8110[76].

2.12 SANDS

With the benefit of experience there is a suspicion here that the working group may have broken its own rule and specified the impossible ! Note for Guidance (i) states:

> "The requirement for sands to be washed is additional to the
> requirements of the Standards, but is in line with the main conclusion
> of CIRIA Report R59 - 'Building Sands: Availability, Usage and
> Compliance with Specification Requirements'."

It is suggested that the requirement for all sands to be washed may not be followed to the letter on all contracts that incorporate CESWI. However, it is quite possible that any future consideration of this will be overtaken by the need to specify the unamended provisions of a harmonized European Standard (see Chapter 9).

2.15 CEMENT

The Notes for Guidance associated with this clause reflect the developing scene regarding cement and it will be noted that, not only have they been brought into line with the latest revision of BS 5328: Part 1, but reference has also been made to BRE Digest 363[77], the latest source of advice as regards sulfate and acid resistance of concrete in the ground.

A new sub-clause 4 has been added, requiring blastfurnace slag cement for the in situ lining of water mains to conform to WIs No. 4-13-01[78]. The reasons for this are explained later on in this chapter, when the extended Section 9 of CESWI is described.

2.24 PRECAST CONCRETE PRODUCTS

This is another example of an omnibus clause but, regrettably, one which is often quoted selectively. The earlier introduction to the analysis of Section 2 explained the water industry's policy towards the production of British Standards that concern it and why, in consequence, it is not sought to amplify the requirements of such standards. This lies behind the proviso in sub-clause 2, but it seems that the wording could be improved.

Some documents prepared for tenderers have included Supplementary Clauses demanding that certain precast concrete products conform to the *"surface finish"* requirements in Section 4 of CESWI, rather than those in the relevant British Standard, the words *"or described in the Contract"* being used as justification. This often runs counter to what the water industry has accepted at BSI and increases costs. Perhaps sub-clause 2 could have been clarified by amending it to read *"Except where otherwise specified in a relevant British Standard or, in the absence of such a Standard, described in the Contract......."*.

2.27 VITRIFIED CLAY PIPES AND PIPELINE FITTINGS

This clause now calls for a specific decision by those preparing documents for tenderers, though attention has not been drawn to that fact in a new Note for Guidance. Successive editions of CESWI have, where vitrified clay pipes are being used for public sewers (whether combined, foul or surface water), specified "*normal*" type rather than "*surface water*", which are not produced to such a stringent specification. Those preparing tender documents must now decide whether pipes to BS 65[79] are acceptable for use as public surface water sewers, or whether to rely on the provisions of BS EN 295[80].

2.28 CONCRETE PIPES AND FITTINGS

Sub-clause 2 was written for the first edition of CESWI but there is a good case that it is redundant, because additional description rule A2 of CESMM3 requires the relevant British Standard to be stated in item descriptions. BS 5911: Part 100[81] deals only with pipes having flexible joints and, of course, such joints are not available in pipes conforming to BS 5911: Part 110[82].

This clause also requires that concrete jacking pipes must conform to BS 5911: Part 120[83] but that specification only covers reinforced concrete jacking pipes of DN 900 and larger. The relevant BSI committee prepared a major amendment to that Standard, extending it to deal with unreinforced pipes and those less than DN 900, for installation by trenchless construction. However, the Institution was unable to publish the amendment due to the "Standstill" procedure described in Chapter 9.

Rather than waste all the effort that had gone into preparing the amendment, the Pipe Jacking Association (PJA) and the CPA issued a technical bulletin[84] in 1993, using the criteria that had been agreed at BSI. CESWI-4 does not refer to that publication, but it nevertheless serves as a "national" specification, pending the harmonized European Standard for concrete pipes and fittings, which will cover jacking pipes of all sizes.

2.29 STEEL PIPES AND FITTINGS

Although the first edition of CESWI included provisions dealing with steel pipes, the second and third editions included the following Associated Topic at the end of Section 5:

> *"Clauses relating to steel pipelines have been omitted because such projects are infrequent and because contract requirements will vary more than for most other pipe materials. General guidance on this*

topic may be obtained by reference to BS 2971[85], BS 4515[86], BS 5135[87], BS 534[88] and BS 3601[89]."

The working group came to the conclusion that this message was no longer valid and so once again set about drafting appropriate clauses. The decision in August 1988 by the sole UK manufacturer of glass composite concrete pipes and fittings to phase out production gave the working group the opportunity to reinstate a specification for steel pipes, together with Notes for Guidance, without altering the adjacent clause numbers !

2.31 DUCTILE IRON PIPES AND FITTINGS

All ferric materials are subject to corrosion and protection systems fall into two categories. Passive physical barriers isolate the metal surface from the corrosive environment, while active protection systems are either based on cathodic protection or chemical passivation of the bare metal surface.

In December 1992 a major new WIs[90] was issued, in which requirements for factory applied polymeric anti-corrosion (barrier) coatings were specified; the following month saw the publication of an associated IGN[91]. Although of significant importance, polymeric barrier coatings are not the standard way of protecting ductile iron pipes against corrosion, but the working group felt it appropriate to refer to the WIs and IGN in a new Note for Guidance.

2.32 UNPLASTICIZED PVC PIPES AND FITTINGS

This clause is an excellent example of the way in which CESWI mirrors the considerable effort that the water industry devotes to the development of materials standards. The reference to BS 3505[92] has been retained, but a new table has been included to give prominence to WIs 4-31-06[93], which not only specifies metric blue PVC-U pressure pipes (as opposed to imperial grey) but also, as the new Note for Guidance explains, calls for higher fracture toughness values than those required by BS 3505.

2.35 ACRYLONITRILE-BUTADIENE-STYRENE (ABS) PIPES AND FITTINGS

This clause has been included in successive editions of CESWI, but there is surely a case that it fails the "norm" test. Can it truly be said that ABS pipes can be found on most water services contracts in England and Wales?

2.36 POLYETHYLENE PIPES AND FITTINGS

The development of WIs's associated with polyethylene pipes, joints and fittings has continued since the publication of CESWI-3. Therefore, the opportunity has been taken to restructure this clause to take account of WIs No's. 4-24-01[94], 4-32-06[95], 4-32-09[96] and 4-32-13[97].

2.40 SERVICE SIZE WATER FITTINGS AND APPLIANCES

The heading of this clause was originally *"Water fittings"*, since it is aimed at building works, as included for the first time in CESWI-2. However, the working group felt that a more accurate title would be *"Service size water fittings and appliances"*, so this change has been made and followed through into the text.

The extensive table of specified requirements for water fittings and appliances has been updated, with particular reference to new specifications for compression fittings[98,99], underground stopvalves[100] and ferrules[101].

2.46 JOINT SEALS AND LUBRICANTS

The heading of this clause and the text reflect the fact that BS 2494[102] now refers to *"joint seals"* instead of *"joint rings"*. Also, a new Note for Guidance has been added, referring to IGN No. 4-40-02[103] for further guidance on the selection, properties and use of elastomeric seals and sealing components.

The original Note for Guidance referring to IGN No. 4-40-01[104] has been retained, but it is rather disconcerting to note that Issue 2 (August 1986) of that IGN remains unaltered. Clause 3.11 includes the following advice:

> *"It is advisable to lubricate the rings evenly with a lubricant suitable*
> *for use with the rubber compound from which the rings are made."*

Although the following sentence of the IGN goes on to advise that the manufacturer should be contacted for his recommendations, the above advice implies that <u>all</u> rings should be lubricated. This is most certainly not true for the rolling ring type of joint, for the consequences of doing so could be dire !

2.49 VALVES

Sub-clause 2 deals with valve parts, either metallic or non-metallic, that are to be in contact with potable water. It has been updated to reflect the fact that DD 201[105] now gives provisional requirements for the suitability of metallic materials, pending the availability of sufficient experience on which to base a British (or European) Standard.

There appears to have been some confusion in the changes that have been made to the requirements for non-metallic materials. CESWI-3 referred to BS 6920: Part 1[106], which specifies limits in the water of turbidity, colour, taste, microbiological growth, metals and extraction of materials into the water. Part 2 deals with the various methods of test that are to be used in connection with Part 1 and so it is not necessary, as has been done in CESWI-4, to change *"BS 6920: Part 1"* to *"BS 6920"*.

Reference has also been added in the new table in sub-clause 2 to IGN No. 5-01-02[107] and this seems to be an error, since it should properly be in a new Note for Guidance.

2.50 PIPE SURROUND MATERIALS

In a 1972 Circular[108] the DoE advised that mechanical pipe joints for public sewers should be the norm after May 1974 but, following representations by the Clay Pipe Development Association, a subsequent DoE Water Authorities Circular[109] advised that this could be deferred to May 1975. The first edition of CESWI therefore assumed that all sewers would have flexible joints and that most of the pipelines would be laid on granular bedding.

The specification for *"pipe bedding and fill material"* (as it was originally called) in the first edition of CESWI was based on the recommendations of successive Government working parties but, in 1980, an IGN[110] brought together the knowledge then available on granular bedding materials for buried pipelines. Successive editions of that IGN and CESWI proceeded to leap-frog each other in a most unsatisfactory way. However, the publication of CESWI-4 was programmed to coincide not only with the latest issue of the IGN[111], but also with the new WIs[112], by which specified requirements for what are now called *"bedding and sidefill materials"* have been separated out from associated guidance.

The CESWI clause has, therefore, been completely rewritten and, for the first time, prescribes requirements that are not only clear, but which have been agreed by representatives of manufacturers of both rigid and flexible pipes.

2.54 SEWER LININGS

CESWI-3 introduced a section on *"Sewer renovation"* and there has since been much development in this area. This clause now reflects the WIs's specifying requirements for precast and in situ ferrocement[113] and non-circular polyethylene[114] sewer linings.

2.55 PRECAST CONCRETE MANHOLES AND SOAKAWAYS

This clause amplifies the requirements of BS 5911: Part 200[115], by demanding that:

> *"Units which bed onto bases shall be manufactured so that imposed vertical loads are transmitted directly via the full wall thickness of the unit. For joints between units and the underside of slabs, joint profiles shall be capable of withstanding applied loadings from such slabs and spigot-ended sections shall only be used where the soffit of the slab is recessed to receive them."*

These performance requirements are designed to ensure that the relevant joints and ends are as cast by the manufacturer. They can be inferred from BS 5911: Part 200 but, nevertheless, have the manufacturers' support.

2.57 MANHOLE COVERS AND FRAMES

The specified minimum clear opening of 600 mm is as recommended in *"Safe Working in Sewers and at Sewage Works"* but, as the Note for Guidance infers, there is no common policy throughout the water industry as to whether circular or square openings are to be used. However, since square openings are normally preferred, BS 5911: Part 200 provides only for 600 mm square openings in cover slabs designed to fit onto DN 900 shafts, these being equally able to accommodate 600 mm circular openings in manhole frames.

2.58 MANHOLE STEP IRONS

Although there are now several alternatives to the traditional galvanized iron single step, the clause heading has unfortunately not been changed. Nevertheless, the options now available have been reflected by new references to Parts 2[116] and 3[117] of BS 1247, together with WIs No. 4-33-01[118]. These not only cover the type of material and any protective coating, but also the type of step, which may now be a double one.

2.59 GULLIES AND GULLY COVER SLABS

The reason for the new choice of Standards was explained in relation to Clause 2.27.

2.63 PRECAST CONCRETE SEGMENTS FOR TUNNELS AND SHAFTS

This is perhaps the longest clause in the "Materials" Section and the reason for that is not hard to find - there is no associated British Standard ! The text was developed to reflect the various types of bolted and unbolted segments that are commonly in use throughout the country, including the specified dimensions and tolerances.

2.74 HANDRAILS AND BALUSTERS

Sub-clause 2 assumes that mild steel and aluminium handrails and balusters are to be respectively hot dip galvanized and anodized. There is perhaps a case that a Note for Guidance is called for, advising that any other form of corrosion protection should be described in the Contract.

2.77 FIXINGS FOR METALWORK

The whole area of fixings for metalwork is a complex one, with a multitude of proprietary fixings available. In consultation with manufacturers the working group sought to produce not only a clause that would specify requirements for the type of fixings most commonly found, but also Notes for Guidance that would advise those preparing documents for tenderers, and those involved in Site supervision, about the latest sources of accepted good practice. In turn, this links in with the requirements of Clause 2.3 concerning the handling and use of materials.

It appears from comments received on earlier editions of CESWI that the provisions of this clause and its associated Notes for Guidance are not always followed, perhaps in the mistaken belief that the selection and use of fixings is not an activity that requires much watching and supervision. If so, that would be most unfortunate.

2.116   GENERAL FILLING MATERIALS

The new sub-clause 2 was originally to be found in Clause 2.50, but it has been moved into this re-titled clause as part of the general process of clarifying the situation as regards pipe surround materials. Clause 2.50 now deals only with materials in the vicinity of the pipeline and requirements for the remaining *"selected fill"* moved to here.

2.117 GRANULAR SUB-BASE MATERIAL

Sub-clause 2 has been updated to reflect the fact that the *"Specification for the Reinstatement of Openings in Highways[119]"*, produced by the Highways and Utilities Committee (HAUC) for use under the provisions of the New Roads and Street Works Act 1991, specifies that the method for determination of frost heave is to be in accordance with BS 812: Part 124[120], as amended by Clause 705 of the DTp's *"Specification for Highway Works"*. It might have been appropriate also to add a new Note for Guidance, paraphrasing the following guidance in the HAUC specification:

> *"The frost heave test described in BS 812: Part 124 is costly and time-consuming and is not suitable for routine on site control checks. The test is primarily intended as a method to establish whether or not an aggregate from a particular source is likely to be frost susceptible when used in road pavement construction. Material for the frost heave test must be representative of the source or sub-grade encountered. Highway Authorities usually maintain a list of 'Approved suppliers of non-frost susceptible materials' and should have a knowledge of frost susceptible type sub-grades in their locality."*

2.124 JOINT FILLER BOARD

The requirements in sub-clause 5 for the composition of preformed filler for joints in concrete structures designed to retain aqueous liquids have been tightened up to include specified criteria for maximum water absorption and non-recovered compression set. Unfortunately the specified reference against which testing is to be carried out is wrong - it should be ASTM D3575[121].

2.125 JOINT SEALING COMPOUNDS AND SEALANTS

Sub-clause 1 now reflects the publication in March 1991 of an important WIs[122], specifying requirements for building and construction joint sealants. Note for Guidance (v) now refers to the first published outcome[123] of a CIRIA laboratory testing programme on the performance of sealant concrete joints in wet conditions, with which the water industry was associated.

SECTION 3 - EXCAVATION, BACKFILLING AND RESTORATION

This Section is perhaps the most dramatic example of the "performance" approach. When the first composite draft was issued for public comment one eminent organisation was moved to point out that requirements for *"excavation"* were covered in under 400 words!

But is this so surprising? Chapter 2 described how, in the light of the Fifth Edition, the working group set its face against telling the Contractor how to do his job and *"Temporary Works"*, which in most instances embrace excavation and backfilling, are the Contractor's responsibility. The presumption that he would work within a framework of accepted good practice was explained in Chapter 7. Specified requirements for excavation and backfilling therefore mainly comprise those that relate to the Permanent Works, or those which have a bearing on the Employer's interests, and this inevitably leads to a much shorter specification than one based on the traditional "method" approach.

The impact of CESMM is also felt on this Section more than most. Chapter 4 described how, thanks to CESMM, the working group was spared the task of developing a specification for *"rock"*, but account had to be taken of terms such as *"Final Surface"* which, although defined in CESMM3 as *"the surface indicated on the Drawings to which excavation is to be carried out"*, can generally be used in the context of Site operations as being synonymous with *"formation"*.

Chapter 9 quoted from the Foreword to CESWI-4 to the effect that some of the principal changes from CESWI-3 reflect the introduction of the New Roads and Street Works Act 1991. Thus the General Note at the start of this Section now includes the following:

> *"In respect of excavation, backfilling and reinstatement in streets this Section incorporates the requirements of the Street Works (Reinstatement) Regulations 1992[124] and the Statutory Code of Practice entitled 'Specification for the Reinstatement of Openings in Highways' June 1992 (the HAUC specification), published by HMSO, both made under Section 71 of the New Roads and Street Works Act 1991."*

Of course, the requirements of the 1991 Act and its associated Regulations impinge on the body that is exercising works powers in streets. It is therefore necessary to ensure, through the Specification, that the Contractor follows the relevant requirements when carrying out any part of the Works that is located in a street.

3.1 EXCAVATION

For the reason given in the introduction to the analysis of this Section, a new sub-clause 2 has been added to this clause, requiring that excavation in *"streets"* must be carried out in accordance with the HAUC specification. Since the word "street" has a particular meaning under the provisions of the New Roads and Street Works Act, it might have been helpful also to include a new Note for Guidance, advising those preparing documents for tenderers that the Contract should describe which, if any, part of the Works are to be constructed in "streets".

It has been suggested that what is now sub-clause 3 is redundant, given that Clause 38(1) of the Sixth Edition provides that:

> *"........the Contractor shall afford full opportunity for the Engineer........to examine foundations before permanent work is placed thereon. The Contractor shall give due notice to the Engineer whenever any such........foundations........are ready or about to be ready for examination....".*

The working group took the view that sub-clause 3 deals with the opposite situation for, if ground in the Final Service is unsuitable, or the Final Surface impaired, then by definition the *"foundations"* are not ready for examination before permanent work is placed on them.

There was much concern in the working group when what is now sub-clause 9 was being drafted, because it appears to give the Contractor a "blank cheque". By T.8.4 of CESMM3 an item must be included in the Bill of Quantities for *"Forward probing"* in tunnels and additional description rule A17 demands that *"the lengths of holes shall be stated in stages of 5 m........in item descriptions for forward probing"*. This sits rather uneasily with the fact that Clause 8(3) of the Sixth Edition requires that *"The Contractor shall take full responsibility for the adequacy stability of all site operations and methods of construction"* and so the working group sought to make that seat a little more comfortable.

The Environmental Protection Act 1990[125] imposes a duty of care on water and sewerage undertakers, whereby they must ensure that any contractor working on their behalf complies with the Act's provisions concerning the treatment, keeping or disposal of excavated material. A new Note for Guidance has been inserted, drawing attention to this situation.

3.5 TEMPORARY DRAINS

The analysis of Clauses 2.50 and 2.116 detailed the background to the simultaneous publication of a revised IGN and new WIs dealing with bedding and sidefill materials for buried pipelines. One of the effects was to do away with the old and confusing references to *"Type A"* and *"Type B"* materials, the former applying to material in the vicinity of the pipeline. There is an echo of this here, in that temporary drains must now be surrounded with *"free-draining granular"* and not *"Type A bedding"* material.

3.7 BACKFILLING

Many Specifications have been written requiring that backfilling is not carried out until a trench and associated pipelaying have been completed between chambers such as manholes - a requirement that was particularly inappropriate where the excavation was in a highway. Sub-clause 1 seeks to recognize the practicalities of life, but it should be appreciated that the term *"specified operations"* includes testing.

Sub-clause 3 has yet another echo of the demise of the confusing *"Type A"* and *"Type B"* materials. Instead of filling materials for *"excavations not situated in highways or prospective highways"* (surely now *"streets"* ?) being required to be *"Type B"*, they are now required to be in accordance with Clause 2.116.2 which, as explained in the analysis of that clause, is actually the same specification as for the original *"Type B"* material.

Sub-clause 4 now requires that the filling of excavations in streets above the level of any pipe surround is to be carried out in accordance with the provisions of the HAUC specification. A new Note for Guidance (ii) reminds those preparing documents for tenderers that there may be situations where particular requirements for the materials to be used for backfilling should be described in the Contract.

3.8 REINSTATEMENT OF MAINTAINABLE HIGHWAYS

The word *"maintainable"* has been inserted into the clause heading so as to align with the terminology of highways legislation, but that is minor surgery compared to what the text of this clause has undergone ! The reinstatement of *"streets which are maintainable highways"*, including carriageways, footways, footpaths, cycle tracks and verges, is now required to be carried out in accordance with the provisions of the HAUC specification.

3.9 REINSTATEMENT OF NON-MAINTAINABLE HIGHWAYS

This new clause flows from the situation that exists in the light of the 1991 Act. It completes the circle as regards the reinstatement of *"streets"*.

3.10 REINSTATEMENT OF UNPAVED LAND

The strangely illogical wording of sub-clause 1 has been adjusted to reflect the actual sequence of events. It has also taken 15 years for someone to spot that sub-clause 2 prescribed "method", so *"cleared"* has now been substituted for *"raked clear"* ! Also in sub-clause 2, the clearing requirement has now been extended to include *"extraneous material"* as well as *"stones"*.

3.14 BLASTING

There is a powerful case that much of this clause has no place in the Specification, given the Contractor's responsibilities under the Sixth Edition. However, the working group took the view that, since any Engineer would demand the kind of things specified where blasting was envisaged, it was appropriate to include them.

ASSOCIATED TOPICS

These remain unaltered and it will be appreciated that the references to BS 6187[126] and BS 8004[127] are to frameworks of accepted good practice.

Chapter 6 described how piling was excluded from CESWI because this type of work, although commonly found on water services works contracts, is covered by the ICE national specification and model procedures. It is nevertheless fair to say that the ICE documents are not prepared on the same basis as CESWI and the suggestion has often been made that clauses covering piling would be appropriate.

At the time CESWI-3 was being finalized, the working group set about preparing a draft *"Piling supplement"*, following the precedent set in the case of well construction. In the event the task could not be fully completed within the time allowed and so the final draft[128] remains on the file, where it waits for someone to pick up the idea.

SECTION 4 - CONCRETE AND FORMWORK

Whilst outlining in Chapter 11 the way in which CESWI has evolved, mention was made of the fact that the concrete and formwork clauses in the first edition were based largely on the recommendations in CP 110 *("Code of practice for the structural use of concrete")*. That code included recommendations concerning concrete as a material, whether Site-mixed or ready-mixed, but March 1976 saw the publication of BS 5328 *("Methods for specifying concrete")*. To the extent that any of the requirements in BS 5328 conflicted with the recommendations of the older CP 110, the working group decided that the former should always prevail.

CP 110 was replaced in August 1985 by BS 8110 and, as explained in Chapter 11, this was one of the major events that prompted the working group to issue Advisory Note No. 1 to CESWI-2. The amendments suggested in that Advisory Note were taken forward into CESWI-3 and CESWI-4, but the latter has also had to recognize the fact that BS 5328 has itself undergone significant changes in recent years, not least that it now comprises four separate Parts[129,130,131,132].

The Foreword to CESWI-2 indicated that *"a significant addition has been the extension of Section 4 to cover structures designed to retain aqueous liquids"*. This was true as far as it went, but the prospect of this type of structure being built using CESWI had been recognized in the Sections of the first edition that dealt with *"Materials"* and *"Testing and sterilization"*, the clauses and Notes for Guidance in those Sections having been drafted to fit with the recommendations of BS 5337: 1976 *("Code of practice for the structural use of concrete for retaining aqueous liquids")*.

By the time CESWI-2 came to be prepared the working group had satisfied itself that the "performance" approach was working well and that it would be appropriate to extend Section 4 to cover such a specialist area as concrete structures designed to retain aqueous liquids. Section 4 was therefore extended to reflect any specialist provisions of BS 5337, as opposed to those of BS 8110 regarding the normal use of structural concrete, but CESWI-3 had to have this Section redrafted to recognize the fact that BS 5337 was replaced by BS 8007[133] in 1987.

The net result of all these changes in the relevant British Standards for concrete and formwork is that the main event which has had to be recognized in CESWI-4 is the splitting of BS 5328 into its four Parts covering the specifying, producing, transporting, sampling, testing and assessing of concrete.

4.1 CONCRETE

The all-embracing requirement in this clause for concrete to be *"produced in accordance with the relevant provisions of BS 5328"* has now been focussed somewhat, in that it must now be *"produced, transported and assessed for compliance with the Specification in accordance with the relevant provisions of BS 5328: Parts 3130 and 4131"*.

4.2 READY-MIXED CONCRETE

Much was made in Chapter 8 about the water industry's commitment to third party certified products, irrespective of the number of licensees that existed. However, after a great deal of debate the working group decided that it would be inappropriate for early editions of CESWI to demand full third party certification in connection with ready-mixed concrete, because of the comparative rarity in those days of plants that could offer the appropriate comfort. It was one thing to contemplate one or two suppliers of Kitemarked materials temporarily serving the water industry until others acquired the necessary certification; it was quite another to think in the same terms as regards ready-mixed concrete !

By the time CESWI-3 came to be prepared the incidence of accreditation had improved dramatically throughout England and Wales and so sub-clause 1 requires that any plant supplying ready-mixed concrete must be approved by a third party certification body accredited under Category 2 ("Product

Conformity") by the NACCB. Remembering the explanation as to why Clause 2.1 provides for "equivalence" in the certification mark and not the certification body, it could be argued that the lack of any provision for equivalence in this sub-clause constitutes a barrier to trade. However, the working group took the pragmatic view that there is not a great deal of ready-mixed concrete imported into England and Wales and that the wording would be reconsidered if any alternative to the established system of accreditation began to emerge.

Sub-clause 3(c) now provides for the delivery ticket to detail the actual cementitious content and the percentage of any pulverized-fuel ash (pfa) or ground granulated blastfurnace slag (ggbs) included in each load of ready-mixed concrete. This is consistent with the optional items in Clause 5.3 of BS 5328: Part 2[130] and the new Note for Guidance (v) draws attention to a further option, whereby the purchaser can specify restrictions on the use of admixtures. There is an important distinction between how these two options have been taken up, in that the Contractor is allowed to supply concrete containing pfa or ggbs, but he does not have *carte blanche* to use admixtures.

4.3 CONCRETE MIXES

Sub-clause 1 now reflects the fact that concrete mixes and their production are covered by BS 5328: Parts 2 and 3 respectively, including the demise of *"ordinary prescribed mixes"*. The additional requirement that *"further information as specified in Clauses 3.2 and 3.3 of BS 5328: Part 3 shall also be given to the Engineer at the appropriate time"* looks innocuous, but it should be borne in mind that the information relates to all of the following:

> Changes in quality assurance of materials;
> Changes in materials;
> Changes in mix composition;
> Cement, ggbs and pfa;
> Changes in concrete quality assurance; and
> Information on admixtures.

The demand for information is also pursued in sub-clause 2, where the working group has now been able simplify the text by simply calling up the provisions of Clauses 3.1 to 3.5 of BS 5328: Part 3, whereby the producer of the ready-mixed concrete must provide the information if requested.

A new sub-clause 6 prescribes normal rates of sampling and is consistent with the general advice in Table 15 of BS 5328: Part 1. Note for Guidance (i) has been amended accordingly and an extra Note for Guidance (viii) added, citing examples from Table 15 of the three types of structure in the new table.

The two remaining amendments in connection with this clause concern Notes for Guidance (iv) and (v). The former has been extended to warn that air-entrainment should be considered for very severe exposure conditions, this being consistent with the advice in Clause 4.3.3 of BS 5328: Part 1, while the latter now also refers to the guidance regarding alkali-silica reaction in Clause 4.2.4 of that Standard.

4.4 TRIAL MIXES

This clause has been repositioned and now reflects the provisions of BS 5328: Part 3 regarding the suitability of the proposed mix proportions of designed mixes to meet the requirements in the Contract for strength and maximum free water/cementitious ratio.

4.8 AIR-ENTRAINED CONCRETE

Now renumbered, this clause now requires that the mean total air content by volume of the fresh concrete at the time of delivery into the construction is to be in accordance with the advice given in Clause 4.3.3 of BS 5328: Part 1 regarding the use of air-entraining admixtures. This has enabled the old Note for Guidance (ii), which referred to the corresponding provisions of BS 8110, to be deleted.

4.9 CHLORIDE CONTENT

This clause (originally 4.8) was conspicuous by the fact that it included specified limits for chloride content, but no means of demonstrating compliance. This has now been remedied by reference to Clause 3.7 of BS 5328: Part 4.

4.10 ADJUSTMENTS TO DESIGNED MIX PROPORTIONS

This clause (originally 4.9) has been extended to demand that the Contractor *"shall provide the details required by Clause 3.2.3 of BS 5328: Part 3 to the Engineer"*. Which is rather strange, because the amendment to Clause 4.3.1 requires the same thing !

4.12 TRANSPORTING, PLACING AND COMPACTING

The publication of BS 5328: Part 3 has enabled sub-clause 1 to be extended to require that the transportation of concrete from the mixer is carried out in accordance with Clause 4.10 of that Standard.

4.13 CONCRETING IN COLD WEATHER

A new condition has been added to sub-clause 1 to the effect that *"temperatures at the surface of the concrete shall be measured where the lowest temperature is expected"*. However, condition (d) already prescribes a performance criterion whereby the surface temperature of the concrete is to be maintained at or above the specified minimum *"at any point"*. It is, therefore, difficult to appreciate the need for this additional requirement which, in any case, requires a subjective decision by unspecified persons !

4.19 STRIKING OF FORMWORK

Sub-clause 2 appears to have undergone major surgery, but much of this is due to restructuring. The principal change to note is that the Contractor is now allowed an alternative criterion to the original one stipulating the minimum period that must elapse before striking vertical formwork. He may now elect to strike if the concrete strength, as confirmed by tests on cubes cured under representative conditions, has reached 5 N/mm^2 (half of that demanded by sub-clause 3 where formwork is supporting concrete in flexure). Should the Contractor elect to go down the original route of minimum periods, it is now made clear that this option relates only to concrete whose cementitious content comprises only Portland cement. At least that is what one supposes is meant by the new phrase *"concrete containing only Portland cement"*!

The same phrase now introduces sub-clause 3 (b), which has a revised and more flexible table based on Table 6.6 of BS 8110: Part 1. However, it is rather strange that the same flexibility has not been provided in Clause 4.15 (*"Curing"*), as provided by Table 6.5 of that Standard.

4.20 SLOPING FORMWORK

This clause has never sat too happily with the provisions of the CESMM and the discomfort continues with the advent of CESMM3 and CESWI-4. A pedantic point is that definition rule D1 in class G of CESMM3 requires angles of inclination of formwork to be classified according to their inclination to the vertical, not the horizontal. However, the continued use of the term *"sloping"* remains correct for the critical inclination specified.

The Note for Guidance is unaltered and states:

> *"Any requirement for top formwork at slopes flatter than 30° to the horizontal should be detailed in the Contract."*

However, measurement rule M3 of CESMM3 class G states:

> *"Formwork to upper surfaces of concrete shall be measured to surfaces inclined at an angle exceeding 15° to the horizontal and to other upper surfaces for which formwork is expressly required."*

SECTION 5 - CONSTRUCTION OF PIPELINES, TUNNELS AND ANCILLARY WORKS

As explained in Chapter 11, this Section was completely restructured during the preparation of CESWI-2, following the decision to include minor building works in the specification. By adding the words *"and ancillary works"* to its title the working group was able to draft the Section in such a way as to cover precast concrete manholes and other concrete chambers, leaving Section 6 to deal with building works.

Section 5 is another prime example of the "performance" approach. When one sits down in front of a blank piece of paper, determined to avoid specifying "method", what does one write about pipelaying? The basic answer is "do it properly within an accepted framework of good practice"; which only leaves the Specification to deal with issues that have a bearing on the Permanent Works. Of course this over-simplifies the situation, but a glance through the various clauses in Section 5 lends support to the point.

In recent years there has been a body of opinion in certain quarters that other Forms of Contract are a more appropriate basis for tunnelling contracts than the ICE Conditions, whether the Fifth or Sixth Editions. Others, apparently still a majority, take the view that the latter provides the most equitable sharing of risks, especially if the promoter has carried out sufficient ground investigation during the preparation of the scheme. Regrettably, this is too often not the case[134], with the inevitable claims due to "unforeseen conditions".

Although its origins lie in the need to disclose all available information, together with the Contractor's responsibility for interpreting this insofar as it relates to the health and safety of people working on the Site (see, for example, the famous *"Penmanshiel"* Case[135]), the new Clause 11(1) in the Sixth Edition is an added facet to the equitable sharing of risks:

> *"The Employer shall be deemed to have made available to the Contractor before the submission of the Tender all information on the nature of the ground and sub-soil including hydrological conditions obtained by or on behalf of the Employer from investigations undertaken relevant to the Works.*
>
> *The Contractor shall be responsible for the interpretation of all such information for the purposes of constructing the Works and for any design which is the Contractor's responsibility under the Contract."*

5.2 PIPE BEDDING

For the reasons explained in relation to Clause 2.50, this clause has been given a new heading and references to *"granular"* bedding taken out of the text.

5.3 CONCRETE PROTECTION TO PIPES

The requirement in sub-clause 3 has now gone full circle. The original requirement was that any concrete protection must be interrupted at each flexible joint and this common sense approach can be traced back through the mists of time to recommendations[136] published in 1964 by the old Building Research Station. The requirement was subsequently changed to *"intervals not exceeding 8 metres"* and there is more than a suspicion that someone was thinking in imperial terms of pipes 8 feet in length! A slightly more generous view might be that it was more in line with current advice[137] of *"not less than about 5m"*. Nevertheless, CESWI-4 has reverted to demanding that any concrete protection must be *"interrupted over its full cross-section at each pipe joint"*!

5.4 COMPLETION OF PIPE SURROUND

Again, the heading and terminology of this clause have been brought into line with the new provisions of Clause 2.50. In sub-clause 1 the finished thickness of fill material above the crown of the pipes has been changed from *"a minimum thickness of 300mm"* to *"250mm"*, this being consistent with the requirements of the HAUC specification.

5.5 PIPELAYING IN HEADINGS

It may be thought that this clause is now something of an anachronism. Most of the pipes laid in headings were concrete ones with, for obvious reasons in the larger sizes, ogee joints. However, to quote from the Foreword to BS 5911: Part 110[138]:

> *"The previous standard referred to the use of products for 'land drainage and sewerage'. Usage now relates to ground water and surface water only; 'sewerage' category pipes having been omitted because of lack of use. Similarly, sizes above DN 1200 have been omitted."*

To coin a phrase, however, reports of the death of headings are exaggerated. They are still sometimes used where a small diameter pipeline needs to go under an obstruction, but even here modern techniques such a microtunnelling are now fast becoming the norm. The headings in such cases are sized to allow working space, as opposed to the pipe and its surround, so the use of pipes with standard flexible spigot and socket joints presents no problems.

5.6 THRUST BLOCKS

Sub-clause 1 has been extended slightly to recognize the fact that welded steel pipelines are once again covered by the specification and so these have also been excluded from the requirement to cast thrust blocks.

5.11 WELDED JOINTS IN STEEL PIPES

As described earlier, clauses relative to steel pipelines have been reinstated in CESWI-4; this clause is one of them and causes the numbers of subsequent clauses in this Section to be increased by one.

It might be thought that the provision in sub-clause 4 whereby the Contractor is required to submit (to the Engineer?) details of his proposed welding procedures is covered by Clause 14(6) of the Sixth Edition. However, the working group took the view that, since this will always be required where a contract calls for welded joints in steel pipes, it would be helpful for it to be included.

5.12 CEMENT MORTAR JOINTS

It really is amazing how requirements that are plainly "method" can go unnoticed for many years. Now that they have been spotted, the words *"with a proper caulking tool"* have been quietly deleted !

5.13 RUN LEAD JOINTS

Flushed with its success at rooting out "method" from Clause 5.13, the working group moved on to find *"with proper irons"* and *"with proper caulking tools"* lurking in this clause. That can no longer be said.

5.14 PROTECTION OF FERROUS PIPES, JOINTS AND FITTINGS

The original requirement in sub-clause 2 regarding each type of external protection for bolted joints and fittings was as follows:

> *"The joint or fitting shall be wrapped with two separate layers of approved protective tape wound spirally with a minimum half width overlap."*

This turned out to be ambiguous. Given the requirement for a minimum half width overlap, the net result must always be two *"layers"*; but were they *"separate"* ? Did the clause really demand two separate applications which, in fact, would result in four *"layers"* once the overlap was taken into account? Whatever conclusion others may have come to in interpreting the original wording, the working group has now sought to clarify the situation by referring to *"two separate applications"*.

The remainder of the clause has been restructured to reflect current practice and to recognize the fact that steel pipelines are once again covered by the specification.

5.15 CUTTING PIPES

A short but significant addition has been made to sub-clause 1. The ends of cut pipes are now required to be sealed - a good example being reinforced concrete ones, where reinforcement is exposed on cutting. A new Note for Guidance links the general requirements of this clause to the specific ones in Clause 5.11 for welded steel pipes.

5.16 PRECAST CONCRETE MANHOLES

As with the heading to Clause 2.58, sub-clause 1 should now refer to *"steps"* and not *"step irons"*, given the enlarged scope of BS 1247 and the provisions of WIs 4-33-01.

Sub-clause 3 maintains the presumption that manholes may be designed, or required, to have a concrete surround. Although special circumstances apply where a manhole is subjected to the passage of site traffic loadings, concrete surrounds have not been recommended for universal application since 1968, following publication of the old CP 2005 *("Code of practice for sewerage")*; this continues in its successor, BS 8005: Part 1[139].

5.20 PIPES AND JOINTS ADJACENT TO STRUCTURES

BS 8005: Part 1 and BS 5911: Part 100 both give advice on suitable lengths for rocker pipes but, unfortunately, they differ slightly. Sub-clause 2 seeks to be consistent with both. The Note for Guidance has been extended slightly, drawing attention to the fact that (surprisingly to some) BS 8005 does not extend its recommendations for the use of rocker pipes to sizes above DN 750.

A minor change has been made in sub-clause 3 in order to remove the possibility of creating the wrong impression. Where pipelines are laid through a manhole, they are now required subsequently to be *"cut out"*, not *"broken out"*.

5.21 WATERTIGHTNESS OF MANHOLES AND CHAMBERS

This clause includes a phrase that was developed after much debate in the working group. Traditionally, manholes and chambers in the United Kingdom have not been required to have flexible watertight joints; indeed, brick manholes are still constructed in certain situations. All of this will change as the European scene impacts on design and construction criteria but, for the moment, the situation remains the traditional one.

It would, therefore, have been a case of "specifying the impossible" if the working group had drafted a simple performance requirement for manholes and chambers to be *"watertight"*. Faced with the types of construction that were regularly designed in the United Kingdom, the group concluded that what one might loosely call *"damp patches"* were inevitable under certain circumstances. Thus the phrase *"substantially watertight, with no identifiable flow of water penetrating the Permanent Works"* was evolved. It should also be borne in mind that the limits for infiltration prescribed in Clause 7.8 relate to the pipelines including manholes.

5.23 CONNECTIONS TO EXISTING SEWERS

The introductory words to sub-clause 3 have been changed to give more emphasis to the fact that connections by means of saddles or junctions are preferred. This was actually one of the main recommendations in NWC Occasional Technical Paper No. 1[140], but the Note for Guidance referring to that publication has been deleted because it is no longer available.

5.25 PIPE JACKING

Pipe jacking and microtunnelling are now accepted as technically sound and economic alternatives to many other forms of construction. The latter has been defined[141] as:

> *"The use of a steerable remote-controlled tunnel boring machine to allow installation of pipelines up to DN 900 by pipe jacking."*

Virtually all pipe jacks and 95%[142] of microtunnels in the United Kingdom are carried out using concrete pipes and the DN 900 demarcation was chosen because that size is the smallest one in the range of man-entry size concrete jacking pipes in BS 5911: Part 120.

Although BS 8005: Part 3[143] and other codes of practice associated with tunnelling refer to the technique of pipe jacking, there is no specific British Standard. The PJA intends to remedy this situation by publishing its own code of practice[144] for the installation of pipe jacks and microtunnels. Although not a British Standard, the new code will fit well into the approach developed by the working group as regards the Contractor being expected to work within a framework of accepted good practice. Much of the PJA code will draw heavily on research work carried out partly at Oxford University and latterly on water services pipe jacking contracts throughout the country.

5.31 GROUTING OF SEGMENTS

The requirement in sub-clause 1 for grouting of segments to be *"undertaken at least once per shift"* has led to difficulties of interpretation and use in some quarters. Notwithstanding the fact that T.8.3.6 of CESMM3 requires the mass of grout materials (excluding water) to be measured in item descriptions, it has been argued in some places that *"twice (or more) a shift"* is consistent with "at least once per shift". Therefore, a new Note for Guidance (ii) has been added, advising that the Contract should identify any locations where it is required to grout more often than once per shift.

5.33 POINTING OF JOINTS

All traditional cement mortars are subject to shrinkage and this can create problems where they are used to point the joints between segments. This clause now requires the use of a proprietary non-shrink mortar.

5.36 TOLERANCES FOR PIPELINES, SHAFTS AND TUNNELS

When the first draft of the specification was issued for comment, everyone seemed to have their own idea of "reasonable" tolerances, including several who felt that *"zero"* tolerance should be specified, leaving the Engineer to decide what was acceptable ! Of course, this flew in the face of the working group's determination not to specify the impossible.

After much debate the tolerances in sub-clause 1 were agreed and it seems that they have stood the test of time. Although unaltered, it is to be hoped that no-one imagines that the tolerances for microtunnelling need be as large as those specified for pipe jacking !

The original Note for Guidance (ii) read as follows:

> *"Where the avoidance of reverse gradients is critical, suitable limits should be described in the Contract."*

This has now been deleted and replaced by:

> *"Any requirements for more stringent tolerances should be described in the Contract."*

This will be seen by many as a step away from the standardization that CESWI has brought. Any person who, for purely subjective reasons, disagrees with the tolerances in the table because they are "too lax", now has an open invitation to substitute whatever tolerances he or she prefers and this is to be deplored. A similar sort of thing has been done in the Note for Guidance on Clause 4.33, but at least there examples have been given of the kind of objective circumstances that would warrant tighter tolerances on surface finish.

5.37 JUNCTIONS AND LATERALS ON SEWERS

This is a new clause, included in response to requests by those commenting on CESWI-3, but why has what is clearly a matter of "design" been included in the Specification?

5.38 MARKER AND INDICATOR POSTS

Requirements for marker and indicator posts have been included in response to requests.

SECTION 6 - BUILDING WORKS

The decision to include small scale building works in CESWI was made during the preparation of CESWI-2 in response to many requests. Of course, the water industry lets contracts for major building works associated with water and sewage treatment works and these are not usually appropriate for use in conjunction with the Sixth Edition. However, many people took the view that it was entirely appropriate for small scale building works (for example, the superstructure to a pumping station) to be included in what was otherwise a civil engineering contract and, therefore, let in connection with the ICE Conditions. It is pleasing to note that a similar view is now taken relative to CESMM3.

The working group accepted the point and, as has been described earlier, this led to the restructuring of Section 5 and the tailoring of Section 6 to building works. In order to avoid any possible confusion, the working group thought it wise to include a "General Note" at the beginning of the Section, drawing attention to the fact that it was only designed to cover small scale building works to be carried out under the Sixth Edition.

It is fair to say that the effort of producing clauses covering small scale building works was disproportionately high compared to that needed in respect of the other Sections. For example, the first edition of CESWI had 83 clauses in the "Materials" Section, but this rose to 119 with the publication of CESWI-2!

Other problems arose from the "performance" approach. It has been explained how, especially as regards excavation, reference to accepted good practice could usually be achieved by quoting the relevant British Standard code of practice in the associated Notes for Guidance. But it proved more difficult to avoid calling up codes in the specification when the working group came to draft the workmanship clauses covering building works.

Perhaps the best, but by no means the only, example is Clause 6.25 - *"Glazing"*. What else can one specify, except to require that *"Glazing shall comply with the relevant provisions of BS 6262"* ? At least the Contractor, here and in other places where codes of practice have been called up, is usually free to choose his method of working within a framework of accepted good practice.

One other general point should be made about Section 6. Although principally concerned with above-ground building works such as pumping station superstructures or treatment works' mess rooms, it also covers below-ground works where, for example, a brick manhole is to be constructed.

6.1 BRICKWORK AND BLOCKWORK GENERALLY

BS 5628: Part 3[145] covers not only brickwork, but also blockwork and, since the latter is now often used on water services works contracts involving small scale building works, the heading, clause and Note for Guidance (iii) have been amended to reflect this.

A most unfortunate addition has been added to sub-clause 4, by the requirement that *"where cut blocks are required, all cutting shall be carried out with a mechanical cutting disc"*. Faced with reports that the skill of some bricklayers left something to be desired, the working group has added a piece of pure "method". Notwithstanding the fact that many bricklayers can produce the necessary quality of cut, and the fact that not all cuts are visible in the finished face, the new requirement prohibits the use of hydraulic splitters, which are commonly found on building sites and, it can be argued, produce a better job than mechanical cutting discs.

6.2 BRICKWORK AND BLOCKWORK, JOINTING AND POINTING

The clause heading has been extended to cover blockwork, to which sub-clause 1 refers.

6.3 CAVITY WALLS

The new sub-clause 2 now requires that:

> *"Weepholes shall be provided by leaving open perpendicular joints at not greater than one metre intervals in the course immediately above the cavity tray, with not less than two weepholes over each opening."*

It seems possible that this may lead to argument. Is it to be inferred from the phrase *"weepholes shall be provided"* that they must always be provided; or should the clause have begun: *"where required by the Contract...."* ?

6.6 BONDING TO CONCRETE

Once again the text has been extended to provide for blockwork.

6.8 CENTERING AND LAGGING

This clause has also been amended to provide also for blockwork, though it is rarely used in connection with centering and lagging on the water industry's small scale building works.

6.9 BRICKLAYING AND BLOCKLAYING IN COLD WEATHER

Yes, you've guessed it ! Blockwork is now covered.

6.17 EXTERNAL RENDERING

Despite the aberration in Clause 6.1.4, the working group's beady eye has spotted and dealt with yet more "method" that had gone unnoticed in this clause. Quite rightly, mortar must now be *"applied"* and not *"thrown from a trowel"* (how on earth did that ever get through?) and then simply *"levelled"*, as opposed to *"levelled with a straight edge"*.

6.32 PLUMBING

There was much debate when this clause was first drafted as to whether the water authority, as it was then, was subject to the water byelaws as regards its own plumbing works. It has also to be remembered that the Employer will not always be synonymous with *"water undertaker"* and that a new building could be being constructed under many different circumstances. For example:

1.   A sewage pumping station being constructed by a local authority under statutory arrangements for the carrying out of sewerage functions;

2.   A sewage treatment works mess room being constructed by a sewerage undertaker in the area of a statutory water company; or

3.   A water treatment works canteen being constructed in the area of another water undertaker.

In the event the phrase *"and local water undertaking byelaws"* was included.

SECTION 7 - TESTING AND DISINFECTION

The first thing students of CESWI will note when reading this Section in CESWI-4 is that the heading has been changed. The origins of this lie in Clause 1.15.2, which requires the Contractor to comply with the WAA's *"Operational guidelines for the protection of drinking water supplies"* when working in connection with potable water; these define *"disinfection"*, not *"sterilization"*, as a "restricted operation" and so it was felt appropriate to make the corresponding emphasis.

Turning to the wider front of testing generally, the working group has always felt it appropriate to preface this Section with the following General Note, now updated to reflect the Sixth Edition:

> *"The action to be taken in the event of failure to satisfy the tests specified has only been referred to in general terms where the text so requires. See Clauses 36 and 39 of the Sixth Edition."*

This could, in fact, have seen the light of day as an Associated Topic, for it comes close to explaining why clauses or, more correctly, parts of clauses, have been omitted. How many Specifications have sought to tie the hands of the Engineer by the inclusion of clauses saying *"under no circumstances whatsoever will the Contractor................, but if he does, he shall.........."* ? To specify a requirement and a simultaneous presumption of non-compliance is clearly ludicrous, for the Contractor is obliged by Clause 13(1) of the Sixth Edition to construct the Works in strict accordance with the Contract; if he fails to do so as evidenced by the outcome of a prescribed test, Clauses 36 and 39 give the Engineer all the powers he needs to deal with the situation.

There is another area where this Section is perhaps unique within the specification. Consistent with the logic of the DAME rule, CESWI does not seek to formulate accepted good practice, but to reflect it. That is why so many of the Notes for Guidance and Associated Topics refer to other nationally accepted documents. However, when the working group began to draw up criteria for the testing of non-pressure and pressure pipelines and referred to the various codes of practice that had been published, it found a morass of different ways of presenting recommended values - often drawn up by committees specializing in a particular pipe material. The group therefore sought to bring some kind of order to the situation by adopting a standardized approach. Wherever possible though, the criteria were made consistent with those recommended in the various codes of practice, even if presented in a novel way.

7.1 CLEANSING OF PIPELINES

Contractors are no longer required to sterilize water mains before they can be commissioned to supply potable water, but to disinfect them. This fact is now reflected in the clause text.

7.4 TESTING NON-PRESSURE PIPELINES

The trend today is away from referring to "gravity" pipelines, not least because many water mains operate under a gravitational pressure of several bars ! The term *"non-pressure"* has therefore been substituted but, in using this, the working group recognized that the pipeline will no doubt undergo periodic temporary hydraulic surcharge during its operational life.

There is a case that the Note for Guidance advising that the type of test should be described in the Contract has now served its purpose. Additional description rule A3 to class A of CESMM3 demands that: *"Item descriptions for........testing of the Works shall include particulars........of methods of testing"*.

7.5 WATER TEST FOR NON-PRESSURE PIPELINES

As with Clause 7.4, the term *"non-pressure"* is now used in the heading and the text, in preference to the original *"gravity"*. Although, as the Note for Guidance says, the provisions of this clause are consistent with those of BS 8005: Part 1, there is a powerful case that the words *"up to and including 750 mm nominal bore"* are misplaced here; this is a specified requirement and should have appeared in Section 5. Had that been done, the working group could have considered whether to limit the prospect of water tests to pipelines constructed in trench.

7.6 AIR TEST FOR NON-PRESSURE PIPELINES

The anomaly described in relation to Clause 7.5 regarding the size limit on specified requirements is compounded here, in that the casual reader might assume, having read Clause 7.5, that air testing is required for all pipelines, irrespective of their nominal bore. Once again, the heading and the text now use the term *"non-pressure"*.

7.7 CCTV INSPECTION OF PIPELINES

The wording of sub-clause 1 is deliberately framed to reflect the varying practices of the former water authorities, and now the water service companies, towards CCTV inspections of new pipelines. Some of them demand (and are prepared to pay for) 100% inspection, while others prefer to judge the situation in the light of circumstances on the Site.

7.8 INFILTRATION

Apart from the change from *"gravity"* to *"non-pressure"*, this clause remains unaltered in CESWI-4. But it is surely doomed.

The clause was drafted in the light of three criteria:

1.   The need to avoid specifying the impossible, in this case total watertightness;

2.   The amount of water that is permitted under the water test, not all of which will simply absorb into the structure of the pipeline; and

3.   The fact that it has been accepted practice for manholes not to have flexible watertight joints, even at the point where pipelines enter the manhole.

All of these were recognized by the old CP 2005 *("Code of practice for sewerage")* which, at the time the first edition of CESWI was being drafted, included the following advice:

> *"The checks after backfilling........should include an infiltration test where the crown of the pipe at the high part of the line under test is more than 1.2 m below the water table.*
>
> *All inlets to the system should be effectively closed. Visual inspection at manholes or inspection chambers will then reveal excessive flow. If the flow is more than a trickle on the invert, investigation of the source will be necessary.*
>
> *The rate of infiltration is dependent upon so many factors that a guide to its permissible extent cannot be given and will depend on the judgement of the engineer."*

The presumption that infiltration might well occur into a brand new system was an anathema to many, not least with regard to its effects on operating costs; but the working group had to draft requirements that reflected currently accepted practice. It came to the conclusion that, in the absence of any other objective yardstick, "whatever is allowed out should be allowed in" - this led to a Note for Guidance, observing that: *"The permissible infiltration is the same as the permissible loss in the water test in Clause 7.5".*

To many this remains an anathema but, as the requirements of European Directives and harmonized standards begin to take effect, the limit on the amount of infiltration permitted into new systems will surely become more stringent.

7.11 DISINFECTION OF WATER MAINS

The heading, text and Note for Guidance of this clause have all been changed to reflect the fact that contractors no longer *"sterilize"* water mains, but *"disinfect"* them.

7.12 CLEANSING OF STRUCTURES

Once again, sub-clause 1 now presumes that *"disinfection"* instead of *"sterilization"* will have been carried out before a structure designed to retain potable water is cleansed.

7.13 TESTING OF CONCRETE STRUCTURES DESIGNED TO RETAIN AN AQUEOUS LIQUID

The requirements of this clause have gone hand-in-hand with those of successive revisions of the associated British Standard code of practice. When the working group first drafted the clause there was widespread dissatisfaction throughout the water industry about the way in which the permitted loss of water was to be measured when testing for watertightness. It was decided that, pending review of BS 5337 *("Code of practice for the structural use of concrete for retaining aqueous liquids")*, the loss should be specified as a proportion of the average depth and, in the event, this was recognized in an amendment to that Standard; also in its successor, BS 8007.

Sub-clause 1 now makes it clear that the period of 21 days for stabilisation must be allowed by the Contractor. Also, the method of recording the water level has been reduced to a performance one.

7.14 TESTING OF ROOFS

It should be noted how Note for Guidance (ii) is consistent with the approach taken towards retesting and described in the introduction to the analysis of this Section.

7.15 DISINFECTION OF STRUCTURES FOR POTABLE WATER

Here is the final example of a heading, clause and Note for Guidance being adjusted to recognize that the Contractor no longer undertakes sterilization.

7.16 GROUT QUALITY CONTROL TESTING

The heading and much of this clause look new, but this is deceptive. When the requirements appropriate to sewer renovation were being drafted for inclusion in CESWI-3 it was decided that those relative to grout quality control testing should be split, on the grounds that the method for testing grout strength fell properly to Section 7, whereas the quality control requirements were appropriate to Section 9. This decision was reviewed during the preparation of CESWI-4 and the performance requirements in the original Clause 9.13 have now been moved to Clause 7.16, along with the associated Note for Guidance.

ASSOCIATED TOPICS

Although it has appeared in successive editions of CESWI, there is an argument that Associated Topic 1 *("Testing of operational equipment")* may be redundant. As explained in Chapter 4, the aim in CESWI is to include advice relative to the CESMM only where there may be thought to be doubt. However, A.2.6 of CESMM-3 seems perfectly clear.

Because of the quantities (and thereby the costs) that are often involved, Associated Topic 2 *("Provision of water for testing")* seeks to avoid any misunderstanding about who is responsible for providing the water each time a testing operation requires it. Those preparing documents for tenderers were advised to make this responsibility quite clear.

Experience has shown that merely following this advice to the letter can still leave room for argument and so it has been extended in CESWI-4 to suggest that the Contract should also describe the points of supply, the quality and programmed rates of delivery.

SECTION 8 - ROADWORKS

Requirements consistent with the demands of the HAUC specification for the reinstatement of streets are given in Section 3 of CESWI-4 However, it is not usual for water services works contracts to include the construction of highways which are to be maintainable at public expense.

Nevertheless, roadworks are often required at treatment works, pumping stations and other installations and so it was necessary for the working group to draft appropriate clauses. As the saying goes, it was not necessary to re-invent the wheel and the following General Note was included as a preface to this Section:

> *"This Section is not intended to cover the construction of prospectively adoptable highways but, together with the relevant materials clauses, is based primarily on the requirements of the Department of Transport's 'Specification for Highway Works'; abbreviated and simplified to take account of the type of road normally required in association with water industry work."*

It was also felt that there would be benefits from a common approach to roadworks construction.

The Section is almost entirely unaltered in CESWI-4, except for two minor points:

8.2 SUB-BASE CONSTRUCTION

In sub-clause 1 the term *"Constructional Plant"* has been changed to *"Contractor's Equipment"*, in order to align with the Sixth Edition.

8.9 LAYING CONCRETE CARRIAGEWAYS

In sub-clause 2 the working group has deleted the requirement for a brushed finish to the concrete surface to be achieved *"with a medium textured wire broom"* on the grounds that here was another bit of "method" that had slipped through the net ! In fact, this point was appreciated when the clause was first drafted, but was deliberately left in because without it there is less control on the consistency of texture provided by the Contractor.

SECTION 9 - SEWER AND WATER MAIN RENOVATION

Both CESMM and CESWI have mirrored the developing technologies of sewer and water main renovation. Chapter 11 described how a Section dealing with the former was included in CESWI-3 in response to many requests and this has been extended in CESWI-4 to cover water main renovation, following publication of the Water Mains Rehabilitation Manual[146] and the correspondingly widened scope of class Y in CESMM3. As might be expected, therefore, the General Note prefacing the Section has been altered drastically in CESWI-4, mostly due to the fact that water main renovation is now covered. However, the surgery does not stop there !

Renovation work, whether for sewers or water mains, often involves a proprietary system and not all are suitable for use in connection with the Sixth Edition. Indeed, some contractors offer their own conditions of contract. Given the fact the CESWI is inextricably linked with the Sixth Edition, the original General Note included the following warning:

> *"This Section covers the fundamental requirements of sewer renovation works to be carried out under the Fifth Edition of the ICE Conditions of Contract."*

The warning has now been deleted, but the following advice has been retained:

> *"Whenever a proprietary renovation system is offered, a described methods statement should be called for and its suitability assessed before acceptance of the Tender."*

Crucially though, the advice in CESWI-3 went on as follows:

> *"The Contract should expressly provide that the Employer is not responsible for the methods of construction."*

The above was included in CESWI-3 as a direct result of the *"Grimwith"* Case[147], so that those compiling contract documents could prevent the Employer from shouldering responsibilities that properly belong with the Contractor. The advice has now been deleted.

A new paragraph has been added, advising that special requirements should be included in the Contract where abnormal conditions exist.

9.1 ISOLATION OF FLOWS

The original clause *("Sewer flows")* has been widened in scope and given a broader heading, together with a new Note for Guidance (iii) advising that the Contract should describe the circumstances under which the Contractor will be permitted to operate valves and isolate flows.

It should be noted that the original wording presumed that flows would be isolated unless otherwise described in the Contract, but the option whether to do this or deal with them *"positively"* now rests with the Contractor. Of course, given the proprietary nature of most renovation work, the method of dealing with flows will usually be assessed before acceptance of the Tender, in accordance with the advice in the General Note.

9.2 PREPARATORY SURVEY

In its previous life this was Clause 9.5 and, of course, related only to sewers. The original requirements remain basically the same but, instead of having to *"note"* the data relative to each lateral, the Contractor must now *"determine"* it.

A parallel requirement, to apply when water mains are to be renovated, has been added as sub-clause 2, though the working group did not think it necessary to include the phrase *"to an accuracy appropriate to the method of reconnection"*. The new sub-clause 4 requires that valves and hydrants are to be checked to ensure that all are accessible and operable, it being left to the Engineer to decide on appropriate action if any are found wanting.

Although CESWI-3 required a survey of the sewers to be renovated, it was silent on whether this should extend to a structural condition survey, which may well have been carried out already and be the trigger for the renovation contract. The new sub-clause 3 and its associated Note for Guidance seek to clarify the situation as regards structural condition surveys, whether for sewers or water mains.

9.3 PREPARATION OF EXISTING SEWERS AND WATER MAINS

This clause and its heading have been extended to embrace water mains. Also, a new Note for Guidance has been added, as per Clause 9.1, concerning the operation of valves and isolation of flows; unfortunately, it has migrated northwards into Clause 9.2 !

9.4 JOINTING GENERALLY

Some people have suggested that this clause, originally Clause 9.4, is redundant, because it is virtually identical to the first sentence of Clause 5.7.1. The error of that suggestion lies in the use of the word "virtually", for the first word of Clause 5.7.1 is *"Pipe"* !

9.5 CONNECTIONS

Originally Clause 9.8, the scope of this clause has been extended to include branches and service connections. Minor adjustments to the text of sub-clause 2 have enabled its provisions to apply equally to the renovation of water mains. Deletion of the modifier *"polyethylene"* from sub-clause 3 has widened the scope of sliplinings covered.

9.6 INTERMEDIATE CHAMBERS

By substituting *"chambers"* for *"manholes"* in this clause (originally Clause 9.10) and its heading, the scope has been widened to include water mains and, for that matter, any chambers other than manholes on sewers. Insertion of the words *"where applicable"* in the text recognizes that treatment to the edges of linings is not always necessary.

9.7 RELEASE OF CURING WATER

Formally Clause 9.11, the scope of this clause has been widened by the simple expedient of substituting *"lining system"* for *"sewer lining"*.

9.8 ANNULUS GROUTING GENERALLY

Now renumbered from Clause 9.12 this clause remains basically intact, though minor modifications have been made. Some of the grout injection pressures used in proprietary systems now exceed 50 kN/mm^2 and so this has been recognized in sub-clause 2 and the new Note for Guidance. Also, the requirement in sub-clause 2 for records of grout quantities and maximum pressures to be made available to the Engineer has been deleted. The former is covered by Clause 56(3) of the Sixth

Edition, but it is not clear where the Engineer's powers now lie for demanding information concerning the latter.

9.9 INSPECTION AFTER GROUTING

This was originally Clause 9.9 and minor amendments to the text have enabled its scope to be extended to cover the renovation of water mains.

9.10 LINING THROUGH VALVES

This is a new clause, necessitated by the inclusion of water main renovation. Clearly, it has to be demonstrated that valves which have been lined through can continue to operate freely. The prohibition on in situ lining through *"non-man entry"* sizes (though just like Clause 9.15 in CESWI-3 these are not defined, nor described in a Note for Guidance) will often have been highlighted when assessing the suitability of a system before a Tender is accepted. However, this has been included as a fall-back provision.

9.11 INSPECTION AFTER RENOVATION

Although the scope of this clause (formally Clause 9.15) and its heading have been widened to accommodate water mains, the requirements of sub-clause 1 have been made less specific and Note for Guidance (i) amended to advise that any requirement for a CCTV survey should be detailed in the Contract.

Sub-clause 2 and Note for Guidance (ii) introduce provisions for the sampling of completed renovation.

9.12 BRINGING RENOVATED WATER MAINS INTO SERVICE

The requirements of this new clause are consistent with the existing provisions where water mains have been laid, modified to reflect the fact that the Contractor is no longer required to *"sterilize"*, but to *"disinfect"*.

13 - POSTSCRIPT

Those who have ploughed through to this point may recall that CESWI was not the first national specification to cover water services works contracts in the United Kingdom. Setting aside those developed by consulting engineers, that honour belongs to the SDD specification.

Logically, there is no reason why there should not be a standard specification for use throughout England, Northern Ireland, Scotland and Wales, because the other reference publications used by those compiling documents for tenderers are virtually the same throughout the United Kingdom. When the process of revising CESWI-3 was put in train the Chairmen of the working groups responsible for the two specifications, along with their respective Technical Secretaries, met to discuss the possibility of collaboration.

The benefits of co-operation were quickly established, but one problem was the fact that CESWI was an an avowedly "performance" specification. The situation relative to the SDD specification (or SADWSS specification as it is now known, being prepared under the auspices of the Scottish Association of Directors of Water and Sewerage Services) was less clear cut and this can best be explained by the following extract from the Foreword to the third edition[148]:

> "Initially the Working Party gave consideration to the form of the revised document with much discussion as to whether the document should be of a method or performance specification. A decision was however taken to keep the previous form of specification which had been well tried and met the needs of most authorities for the majority of their contracts. Notwithstanding it was agreed to make fairly radical changes if felt necessary. As a result certain sections of the previous document have been eliminated or consolidated with other sections and new sections such as those of Tunnelling and Pipejacking, Metal Structures, Cladding and Painting and Reconditioning of Mains and Sewer Renovation were incorporated."

Of course, the view from south of the border was that the "performance" approach had now stood the test of time. Indeed, there is little or no prospect of CESWI reverting to a "method" approach.

Although the professional expertise and independence of each group was accepted, it was felt appropriate to continue the dialogue that had been started. Accordingly, in July 1992, the Chairman of the CESWI working group was authorized to invite his opposite number to nominate two "observers" to sit in on the preparation of CESWI-4; one would be drawn from the Scottish regional councils, who are responsible for the provision of water and sewerage services in Scotland, the other from the DoE Northern Ireland Water Executive, which was represented on the SADWSS working party.

The two observers duly sat in on the proceedings, not only of the CESWI working group itself, but also of two of its sub-groups. In due course the present third edition of the SADWSS specification will come up for review and at that time the working party will no doubt have before it the views of the two observers on CESWI-4. Viewed from south of the border, it would be a major step forward if the working party decided to recommend to SADWSS that the time was ripe for a full United Kingdom specification. Of course, many factors will have to be taken into account, not all of them technical, and the prospect does rather presume that the water service companies and the statutory water companies will continue to have faith in the benefits that flow from a common approach. We shall all just have to wait and see.

80

ANNEX
MILESTONES

The following is a summary of the important milestones along the road that started with the landmark decision at that first meeting of the NWC Directors of Operations' Group:

April 1974	-	NWC Directors of Operations' Group establishes specifications working group.
July 1974	-	Working Group holds first meeting under Chairmanship of H S (Bert) Tricker (NWC).
March 1977	-	First composite draft specification issued for public comment.
July 1977	-	Wilfrid F George (NWC) assumes Chairmanship of working group.
July 1978	-	CESWI published by NWC.
October 1978	-	John K Budleigh (Southern Water) assumes Chairmanship of working group.
October 1980	-	CESWI - Advisory Note No.1 published by NWC.
October 1981	-	CESWI - Advisory Note No.2 published by NWC.
April 1982	-	NWC Directors of Operations' Group endorses preparation of CESWI-2.
June 1982	-	WRc assumes Secretariat of working group.
October 1983	-	WAA succeeds NWC.
July 1984	-	CESWI-2 published by WRc on behalf of WAA.
October 1985	-	Haydn White (Yorkshire Water) assumes Chairmanship of working group.
August 1986	-	CESWI-2 - Advisory Note No.1 published by WRc on behalf of WAA.
July 1987	-	WAA Environmental and Technical Group endorses preparation of CESWI-3.
May 1989	-	CESWI-3 published by WRc on behalf of WAA.
September 1989	-	WSA succeeds WAA.
October 1991	-	CESWI-3 - Advisory Note No.1 published by WRc on behalf of WSA.
June 1992	-	WSA Water Services Management Group endorses preparation of CESWI-4.
June 1992	-	CESWI-3 - Advisory Note No.2 published by WRc on behalf of WSA.
April 1993	-	Brian Spark (Anglian Water) assumes Chairmanship of working group.
October 1993	-	CESWI-4 published by WRc on behalf of WSA.

APPENDICES

The following Appendices contain guidance regarding the additional information that CESWI-4 suggests should be provided in contract documents and have been drafted by Brian Spark, the current Chairman of the CESWI Working Group. The Appendices follow the order of the Sections in CESWI-4 and contain both details of the information that is to be provided and suggestions for where in the contract documents it should be located.

A checklist column has been provided in the Appendices to help in their use as an *aide - mémoire* to those preparing contract documents.

Brian Spark is a Chartered Civil Engineer with 35 years experience in the UK water industry, the majority of this time spent in managing the design and construction of capital works. He has worked for Anglian Water since it was formed in 1974 and had responsibility for contract and design standards in the Company from 1985 to 1991. Since then he has been the Company Quality Assurance Manager and has been responsible for the introduction of quality management systems in Anglian Water Services Limited for drinking water sampling and water supply. He has been active in water industry contract conditions and engineering specifications work since 1985 including Form G90, Form P and the Civil Engineering Specification for the Water Industry. He has been Chairman of the Water Services Association CESWI Group, which produced the 4th Edition, since April 1993. He represents the WSA on BSI committees concerned with cement and lime and on the ICE Site Investigation Steering Group.

Appendix 1 - Supplementary guidance for Section 1 - General

Clause	Description	Information to be provided	To be included in	Check
1.1 NfG (i)	"The Contract should prescribe the extent of the Site, including working areas, accesses and the periods for which they will be available. Reference should be made to any known hazards."	A map or plan of the Site showing areas which are assigned to the Contractor, the routes he must use to gain access. Periods of availability and known hazards could be marked on the map or plan.	Drawings. Availability and hazards may be stated in a Supplementary Clause.	
1.3.1	"Where the type and locations of temporary site fencing are described in the Contract."	Details and locations of temporary fencing which is not required by the Contractor for safety or security purposes. Type and length.	Drawings. Bill items - CESMM class A2.	
1.4 NfG (i)	"The Contract should prescribe the datum level for the Works, together with any master bench marks. Precise reference of the Works to existing features, or to the Ordnance Survey National Grid, should be shown."	The datum level that has been used in the design of the Works. Master bench marks that are to be used by the Contractor. Reference dimensions and levels.	Drawings or Supplementary Clause. Drawings. Drawings.	
1.5.1	"The Contractor shall provide ......accommodation as described in the Contract."	Details of accommodation required.	Supplementary Clause.	
1.5 NfG (i)	"Accommodation descriptions should include any car parking facilities required for the Engineer."	Details of number of car parking spaces required.	Supplementary Clause.	
1.5.2	"Where movable offices are required by the Contract."	Details of movable offices e.g. for contracts involving extensive pipelaying.	Supplementary Clause.	
1.5.3	"Where the Contract requires telephone facilities for the Engineer."	Details of telephone and any facsimile facilities required.	Supplementary Clause.	
1.5 NfG (v)	"If required, insurance of office contents."	Details of any cover to be provided.	Requirement in Special Condition of Contract. Details in Supplementary Clause.	

Clause	Description	Information to be provided	To be included in	Check
1.7 NfG (ii)	"The Contract should describe any special precautions necessary to comply with the Employer's obligations under Sections 3, 4 and 5 of the Water Industry Act 1991 (environmental duties)."	Any special precautions which the Contractor is to take in connection with: (a) furthering the conservation and enhancement of natural beauty and the conservation of flora, fauna and geological or physiographical features of special interest, (b) preserving public access to places of natural beauty, (c) protecting and conserving buildings, sites and objects of archaeological, architectural or historic interest, and (d) maintaining the availability to the public any facility for visiting or inspecting any of these buildings, sites or objects.	Supplementary Clause.	
1.10 NfG (iii)	"Any permanent support known to be required should be described in the Contract."	Details of any permanent support required by a Statutory Undertaker, Highway Authority or other owner for their apparatus.	Bill item - CESMM class K and/or L.	
1.11 NfG (i)	"The Contract should describe any apparatus which requires diverting or removing on account of its interference with the construction of the Permanent Works."	Description of any apparatus requiring diverting or removing, sufficient to allow the Contractor to indicate the timing and/or phasing of the diversions or removals in his programme.	Drawings.	
1.11 NfG (v)	"Any requirements of Statutory Undertakers or public bodies should be described in the Contract."	Any requirements of a Statutory Undertaker or Public Body.	Supplementary Clause.	
1.12 NfG (iii)	"The Contract should include details of any road closures to be arranged by the Employer."	Details of any road closures.	Supplementary Clause.	
1.14 NfG (ii)	"Any requirement for the Contractor to liaise with the appropriate Land Drainage Authority should be described in the Contract."	The details of any requirement including the name of the Land Drainage Authority.	Supplementary Clause.	

Clause	Description	Information to be provided	To be included in	Check
1.15 NfG (ii)	"Provision should be made in the Bill of Quantities for all medical testing required by this Clause."	Any medical testing requirements.	Bill item - CESMM class A2.	
1.16 NfG (i)	"Those guidelines should also be incorporated in any other type of contract where the use of breathing apparatus will be required."	Any requirement on the Contractor to comply with the relevant provisions of the water industry's guidelines for the use of respiratory protective equipment, when work is to be carried out other than in sewers or at a sewage works.	Supplementary Clause.	

Appendix 2 - Supplementary guidance for Section 2 - Materials

Clause	Description	Information to be provided	To be included in	Check
2.3.2	"Unless otherwise described in the Contract, the use, installation, application or fixing of materials and components shall be in accordance with all applicable recommendations of the manufacturers."	Any variations from a material or component manufacturer's recommendations for use, installation, application or fixing.	Supplementary Clause.	
2.6 NfG (iv)	"The required grass seed mixture should be described in the Contract."	Mixture required (1-4) from table in Clause 2.6.1, or special agricultural mixture.	Bill item - CESMM class E8	
2.9 NfG (ii)	"Where potable mains water is not available, alternative provisions should be described in the Contract."	The requirements on the Contractor (or the Employer) for supplying suitable water.	Supplementary Clause.	
2.10 NfG (i)	"Any restrictions on the source, type or group classification of aggregates should be described in the Contract."	Any restrictions that are to apply (e.g. no coal fragments in concrete with visible faces).	Supplementary Clause.	
2.10 NfG (ii)	"Concrete designed to retain an aqueous liquid should be described as such in the Contract."	Description of any concrete as water retaining.	Bill items - CESMM class F.	
2.10 NfG (iii)	"Specific precautions to minimise unacceptable damage from alkali-silica reaction should be described in the Contract."	The precautions from those described in BS 5328: Part 1 Clause 4.2.4 that are to apply.	Supplementary Clause.	
2.15 NfG (i)	"The permitted type(s) of cement should be described in the Contract."	Type(s) of cement or cement/ggbs or cement/pfa combinations chosen from those tabulated in Clause 2.15.1.	Supplementary Clause.	
2.15 NfG (ii)	"The type of cement should be stated in item descriptions for concrete."	Type of cement required.	Bill items - CESMM classes H, I, J, K, L, P, R, S, T and Y.	
2.18 NfG (i)	"The nominal size of [filter] media should be described in the Contract."	The nominal size of filter media required from the sizes in BS1438 i.e. 63 mm, 50 mm, 40 mm, 28 mm, 20 mm or 14 mm. Other sizes may be used but this will be subject to agreement with the filter media supplier.	Bill item - CESMM class E6.	

Clause	Description	Information to be provided	To be included in	Check
2.19 NfG (i)	"The required class of grout together with the type of cement and any admixture, should be described in the Contract."	The required class (G1-G6) from the table in Clause 2.19.1 and any admixture required	Bill items - CESMM classes C, G, T and Y.	
2.21 NfG (i)	"The Contract should describe whether Type 1 (square twisted) or Type 2 (ribbed) high yield bars are required."	Type of bar required.	Bill items - CESMM classes G, R and T.	
2.21.2	"Unless otherwise described in the Contract, [steel fabric reinforcement] shall be delivered to the Site in flat sheets."	Details of any off-site sheet bending and cutting required.	Drawings and Bill items - CESMM class G5.	
2.24.2	"Except where otherwise specified in a British Standard or described in the Contract, the surface finish of precast concrete products shall be Rough Finish for surfaces next to earth and elsewhere Fair Finish."	Any alternative surface finishes required to those already specified.	Bill items - CESMM class H.	
2.27.1	"Vitrified clay pipes and pipeline fittings shall comply with the relevant provisions of BS EN 295 or BS 65 unless otherwise described in the Contract."	The relevant Standard.	Bill items - CESMM classes I and J.	
2.27 NfG (ii)	"The type of joint and jointing materials for extra chemically resistant pipes should be described in the Contract."	The type of joint and jointing materials formulated to be specifically resistant to any chemical effluents to be conveyed.	Bill items - CESMM classes I and J.	
2.28.2	"All pipes and fittings shall have gasket-type joints of spigot and socket or rebated form, unless otherwise described in the Contract." .	Any alternative joint type required.	Bill items - CESMM classes I and J.	
2.28 NfG (i)	"Particular requirements from the options listed in Appendix A of BS 5911: Parts 100, 110 or 120 should be described in the Contract."	Particular requirements chosen from: For BS 5911: Part 100 (a) Quantity and nominal size of units. (b) If any restriction on effective length is to apply.	Drawings and/or Bill items - CESMM classes I and J as appropriate.	

Clause	Description	Information to be provided	To be included in	Check
		(c) Crushing test loads of units, and whether units are required to be reinforced. If crushing test loads higher than those given in table 7 (of BS 5911: Part 100) are required, the maximum load and, for pipes up to DN 300, the BMR value.		
		(d) The classification of exposure conditions for sulfate attack, if higher than class 2.		
		(e) If samples of aggregate and/or evidence of satisfactory performance of concrete made with such aggregates are required.		
		(f) If any restriction on admixtures is required.		
		(g) If main reinforcement in a non-circular arrangement is acceptable.		
		(h) If additional concrete cover is required.		
		(i) If details of internal and external diameter are required.		
		(j) Type of bend required.		
		(k) Dimensions and materials of branch pipes for junctions.		
		(l) The number and type of tests to be witnessed and if any additional tests are required.		
		(m) If the products are to be covered by a third party certification scheme.		
		(n) If units subject to the hydrostatic or works proof load crushing test are not to be produced as part of a continuing series of batches, the specified inspection procedures.		
		(o) If lifting facilities are required for pipes other than those with main reinforcement in a non-circular arrangement.		
		For BS 5911: Part 110 As BS 5911: Part 100 (a) to (n).		
		For BS 5911: Part 120 As BS 5911: Part 100 (a), (d) to (i), (l) and (m) and		

Clause	Description	Information to be provided	To be included in	Check
		(i) Crushing test loads of pipes. The maximum load if crushing test loads higher than those given in table 5 are required. (ii) If lifting holes, grout holes or inserts are required. (iii) Sufficient details for the design of recesses in lead and interjack pipes. (iv) If a statement of the jacking loads for which the pipes were designed is required. (v) The type of joint and material of any collar. (vi) If jacking pipes are not to be produced as part of a continuing series of batches, the specified inspection procedures.		
2.29 NfG (i)	"The required grade and thickness of steel, together with the type and strength of pipe, should be described in the Contract."	Grade depends on type (method of manufacture) of tube as follows: Type Grade Buttwelded 320 Electric resistance including induction welded 320 360 430 Seamless 360 430 Submerged arc welded 430 Thickness depends on the design of the pipeline but the following minimum nominal thicknesses should be observed. Outside Diameter (mm) Min. Nominal Thickness (mm) 406.4 4.5 457 5.0 508 5.0 559 6.3 610 6.3 660 6.3 711 6.3 762 6.3 813 7.1 864 7.1 914 7.1 1016 7.1 1219 8.0 1422 8.8	Bill items - CESMM classes I and J.	

Clause	Description	Information to be provided	To be included in	Check
		Minimum nominal thicknesses for other outside diameters are given in Table 1 of BS 534. Strength of pipe may be expressed as the maximum working pressure.		
2.29 NfG (ii)	"Any requirement for coatings to steel pipes should be described in the Contract."	Any coating chosen from those in Section 5 of BS 534 as follows: External protection Reinforced bitumen sheathing. Bitumen enamel wrapping (filled bitumen with glass tissue). Coal tar enamel wrapping (filled coal tar with glass tissue). Plastics cladding. Internal protection Bitumen lining. Concrete lining. Cement mortar lining. Polymetric anti-corrosion (barrier) coatings to WIs No. 4 - 52 - 01 may alternatively be specified	Supplementary Clause.	
2.30 NfG (i)	"Particular requirements from the options listed in Appendix C of BS 4625 or Appendix A of BS 5178 should be described in the Contract."	For pressure pipes to BS 4625: (1) The type of cement to be used in (a) the core, and (b) the cover coat. (2) Whether or not a bituminous or other approved coating is required. (3) The maximum working pressure. (4) The maximum site test pressure. (5) What pressure (if any) additional to (3) will be encountered due to surge. Either the external crushing test load or the following information: (6) The maximum and minimum depths of cover over the pipe. (7) The width of trench at the crown of the pipe (normally outside dia. of pipe plus 600mm). If the pipe is not to be laid in a trench full details should be supplied.	Drawings and/or Bill items - CESMM classes I and J as appropriate.	

Clause	Description	Information to be provided	To be included in	Check
		(8) Whether more than one pipeline is to be laid in the trench, and if so, what will be the trench width at the crown of the pipe. (9) Details of the backfill material, e.g. sand and gravel, saturated clay, etc., and its density in kg/m^3. (10) Type of bedding material. (11) Anticipated loading superimposed on ground surface. For non-pressure pipes to BS 5178: (a) Quantity and nominal bore of pipes and fittings. (b) Strength class of pipes required. (c) Type of cement to be used. (d) Whether a sample of the aggregate is required. (e) The kind and number of tests required. (f) Whether any variation is to be allowed in the time of maturing. (g) Whether certificates are required as to compliance with the standard and date of manufacture. (h) Whether any protective coating is required and, if so, the type.		
2.30 NfG (ii)	"The Contract should describe whether cylinder or non-cylinder type pipes and fittings are required."	The type required.	Bill items - CESMM classes I and J.	
2.38 NfG (i)	"The Contract should describe the section required for asbestos-cement, aluminium and PVC-U gutters."	Any section required from: Asbestos-cement Half round Valley No. 1 pattern North light valley Boundary wall No.1 pattern Boundary wall No. 2 pattern Box Aluminium Half round Rectangular Ogee PVC-U True half-round Nominal half-round.	Bill items - CESMM class X3.	

Clause	Description	Information to be provided	To be included in	Check
2.38 NfG (ii)	"The Contract should describe the required grade and shape of sheet and strip aluminium pipes and gutters."	The grade required chosen from heavy or light. Gutter and pipe shape as 2.38 NfG (i) as appropriate.	Bill items - CESMM class X3.	
2.38 NfG (iv)	"The Contract should describe whether ears are required on cast iron pipes and fittings."	A requirement for ears if these are to be used.	Bill items - CESMM class X3.	
2.38 NfG (v)	"The Contract should describe the required colour of PVC-U pipes and fittings."	The colour required.	Bill items - CESMM class X3.	
2.40 NfG (ii)	"The required class of plastics service pipes, pump delivery pipes and distributing pipes and fittings should be described in the Contract. Where copper is to be used, the required designation and condition should be described."	The class of any pipes and fittings required and the designation and condition of any copper pipes and fittings.	Bill items - CESMM classes I and J.	
2.42 NfG (i)	"Consideration should be given to the use of a marker tape and any requirements described in the Contract."	Requirements for any use of marker tape. If sewers are to be marked the specification of the tape to be used.	Supplementary Clause in Section 5. Supplementary Clause.	
2.47.1	"Flanges for pipes and pipeline fittings shall, unless otherwise required by the Contract comply with BS 4504 Section 3.1 and 3.2 for 16 bar nominal pressure rating."	Any alternative requirements for flanges.	Bill items - CESMM classes I and J.	
2.48 NfG (i)	"Any requirement for full face gaskets should be described in the Contract."	Any requirement for full face gaskets.	Bill items - CESMM classes I and J.	
2.49 NfG (i)	"Particular requirements from the options listed in the various [valve] Standards should be described in the Contract."	Any particular requirements as to, for example, materials of construction, protective coatings.	Supplementary Clause and Bill items - CESMM class J as appropriate.	
2.50 NfG (i)	"Any limitations on the size and type of materials should be described in the Contract."	Any limitation on the size and type of materials.	Supplementary Clause.	
2.55 NfG (i)	"Particular requirements from the options listed in Appendix A of BS 5911: Part 200 should be described in the Contract."	Requirements as to: (a) Quantity of units and relevant nominal sizes. (b) Type of cover slab required.	Drawings, Supplementary Clause and Bill items - CESMM class K as appropriate.	

Clause	Description	Information to be provided	To be included in	Check
		(c) The classification of exposure conditions for sulfate attack, if higher than class 2. (d) If samples of aggregates and/or evidence of satisfactory performance of concrete made with such aggregates are required. (e) If any restrictions on admixtures is required. (f) If additional concrete cover is required. (g) If details of external diameter are required. (h) The number and type of tests to be witnessed and if any additional tests are required. (i) If step irons are not to be fixed. (j) If the products are to be covered by a third party certification scheme. (k) If shaft and chamber sections are not to be produced as part of a continuing series of batches, the specified inspection procedures for the works proof load crushing test.		
2.57 NfG (i)	"If a particular shape of [manhole] opening is required, this should be described in the Contract."	Any particular shape required.	Drawings and Bill item - CESMM class K.	
2.58 NfG (i)	"For all manholes except the precast concrete type, it will be necessary to describe the size and type of manhole step irons in the Contract."	Single or double size. Type from: Malleable iron Ductile iron Steel Stainless steel Plastic encapsulated steel Plastic encapsulated stainless steel Plastic encapsulated aluminium Aluminium with plastics fixings.	Drawings and Bill items - CESMM class K.	
2.59 NfG(i)	"The Standard which is to apply for vitrified clay gullies should be described in the Contract."	One of either BS EN 295: Part 1 or BS 65.	Bill items - CESMM class K3.	

Clause	Description	Information to be provided	To be included in	Check
2.61 NfG (ii)	"The required type of hydrant, dimensions of surface box frames and covers, and size type and material of hydrant indicator plates should be described in the Contract."	Type from wedge gate (type 1) or screw-down (type 2). Surface box frames and covers from grade A or grade B. Size, type and material of indicator plates as agreed with Fire Authority.	Bill items - CESMM class J.	
2.62 NfG (i)	"Particular requirements from the options listed in Appendix A of BS 5834: Part 1 should be described in the Contract, as should those from Appendix B of Parts 2 and 3."	Requirements as to: BS 5834: Part 1 (a) The type of guard required. (b) The dimensions required. (c) Whether slots are required in vitrified clay guards. (d) What type of foundation unit is required. (e) What type and size of guard the foundation unit is to be used with. (f) Pattern of valve to be used. (g) Whether single or double channel units are required. (h) What material is required. (i) Whether sulfate resisting cement is required. (j) Whether the Employer wishes to inspect the guards and/or foundation units. BS 5834: Part 2 (a) What material is required. (b) If a composite unit is required. (c) Whether sulfate-resisting cement is required. (d) The cover shape required. (e) Whether open or closed keyways are required. (f) What arrangement of the concrete base is required. (g) Whether uncoated boxes are required. (h) What grade of surface box is required. (i) What type of surface box is required. (j) What size of minimum clear opening is required. (k) Whether the Employer wishes to inspect covers and frames prior to the application of coating. (l) Whether the Employer wishes to witness the quality control tests.	Drawings and/or Bill items - CESMM class K as appropriate.	

Clause	Description	Information to be provided	To be included in	Check
		(m) Whether a certificate of compliance with the standard is required. (n) Whether any special marking is required. BS 5834: Part 3 (a), (c), (e), (g) and (k) to (n) of BS 5834: Part 2 requirements plus: (i) Designation of surface box required. (ii) If a composite frame is required. (iii) What shape is required for the base of a composite frame so that it matches the type of concrete sections forming the walls of the particular chamber.		
2.63 NfG (i)	"The required type of cement [for precast concrete segments for tunnels and shafts] should be described in the Contract."	Type of cement from tables in Clause 2.15.1.	Bill items - CESMM class T.	
2.63.10	"Where grouting [of segments] is described in the Contract."	Requirements for any grouting of segments.	Bill items - CESMM class T83.	
2.69 NfG (i)	"The required grade of steel [for steel sheet piles] should be described in the Contract."	The grade of any steel required, BS 4360 weather resistant grades are: WR50A - As rolled WR50B - As rolled or normalised WR50C - As rolled or normalised.	Bill items - CESMM class P.	
2.72 NfG (i)	"Any protective coatings [to nuts, screws, washers and bolts] should be described in the Contract."	Details of any protective coating required.	Supplementary Clause.	
2.74 NfG (ii)	"Where stainless steel tubes [for handrails and balusters] are to be bent to very small radii, it may be necessary to describe their condition as GKM(S) instead of KM."	That condition GKM(S) tubes are required.	Bill items - CESMM class N.	
2.76 NfG (i)	"The information required by Appendix B in each Part of BS 4592 should be described in the Contract."	Requirements as to: BS 4592: Part 1 (a) Where appropriate, scale plans of the area to be covered, indicating: (1) position of all supporting members.	Supplementary Clause and Drawings as appropriate.	

Clause	Description	Information to be provided	To be included in	Check
		(2) direction of the load bearing bars in relation to the flooring layout or walkway. (3) location and size of any cut-outs necessary for columns, cable and pipe openings, etc. (Where pipe movement occurs, also state the limits of the extreme conditions.) (4) location and size of any toe plates to be fixed to flooring or walkway. (b) Type of grating. (c) Type of top surface (plain or serrated). (d) Materials from which the flooring, walkway or stair treads are to be fabricated. (e) Loading for which the flooring, walkway or stair treads are to be designed. For wheel loading, the tread area, maximum wheel load and direction of travel will need to be stated. (f) Any limitations on depth of flooring or walkway. (g) Any limitations on size or weight of flooring or walkway. (h) Any limitation on the use of gratings where the loadbearing bars span a number of supporting members. (i) Whether the flooring or walkway is to be removable. (j) Method of fixing (clips or welding). (k) Whether the flooring or walkway is internal or external to a building and whether any particularly corrosive conditions exist. (l) Type of finish. (m) Conditions affecting the sequence or time schedule of erection of floors or walkways, including heights relative to ground level. <u>BS 4592: Part 2</u> As BS 4592: Part 1 requirements: (a) except: (2) direction of span of the flooring or walkway. (d) to (g), (i) and (k) to (m). Plus:		

Clause	Description	Information to be provided	To be included in	Check
		(i) Any limitations on the use of continuous span panels. (ii) Method of fixing (clamping or welding). BS 4592: Part 3 As BS 4592: Part 1 requirements: (a) except: (2) direction of span of the flooring or walkway. (d) to (g), (i) and (k) to (m). Plus: (i) Any limitations on the use of planks spanning continuously. (ii) Method of fixing (staggered or in-line).		
2.77 NfG (i)	"Sizes and types of fixings (for metalwork) should be described in the Contract, together with minimum requirements for edge distances, centres of fixings and embedments."	Sizes and types of any metalwork fixings. Any dimensional requirements.	Bill items - CESMM class N. Drawings.	
2.77.3	"Where described in the Contract, axial and shear loading tests on structural fixings in concrete or masonry shall be carried out in accordance with the provisions of BS 5080: Parts 1 and 2 respectively. The safe working load shall be as described in the Contract."	Any requirement to carry out the tests and any safe working load that the structural fixing is required to resist.	Supplementary Clause.	
2.83 NfG (i)	"The required thickness, grade and type of bonding [of plywood] should be described in the Contract."	The thickness required. The grade required chosen in accordance with the intended final use as follows: Grade E - Natural surface intended to remain visible. Grades I and B - Surface which may remain visible. Grade II - Surface which may be directly overlaid or painted. Grades III and BB - Surface generally intended to be unseen, painted or coated. Grades IV and C - Surface for which appearance is not the prime consideration. Bond type chosen from: WBP - Highly resistant to weather, micro-organisms, cold and boiling water and wet and dry heat.	Bill items - CESMM classes O and Z.	

Clause	Description	Information to be provided	To be included in	Check
		CBR - Resistant to weather but may fail under prolonged exposure or other demanding conditions of use. MR - To survive full exposure to weather for only a few years. INT - Strong and durable in dry conditions and resistant to cold water, but will not withstand attack by micro-organisms.		
2.84 NfG (ii)	"The required strength class for BS 4978 grades of softwoods should be described in the Contract."	For any softwood to be used for non-structural purposes the strength class required from: SC1 to SC5	Bill items - CESMM class Z.	
2.84 NfG (iii)	"The desired service life category [for timber] should be described in the Contract."	Service life desired chosen from: Category A - 60 years Category B - 30 years	Bill items - CESMM classes O and Z.	
2.86 NfG (i)	"The relevant design reference in BS 1186: Part 3 should be described in the Contract."	The class of any trim required chosen in accordance with its use as follows: Class CSH or Class 1: Timber for high quality or specialised trim. Class 2 and Class 3: Timber for general purpose trim.	Bill items - CESMM class Z.	
2.87 NfG (i)	"The required type and finished thickness of [wood] flooring should be described in the Contract."	The type from softwood or wood chipboard and any finished thickness required from: Softwood 16mm, 19mm, 21mm or 28mm Wood chipboard 6mm to 50mm.	Bill items - CESMM class Z.	
2.88 NfG (i)	"Detailed requirements for doors should be described in the Contract."	Sizes and other details of any doors required.	Drawings and Bill items - CESMM class Z.	
2.88 NfG (ii)	"Particular requirements for wood door frames and linings (except those for fire-check flush doors) should be described in the Contract in accordance with Appendix A of BS 1567."	Appropriate requirements as to: (1) The handling of door frames with winglights (i.e., whether the winglight is on the right or left of the door frame, when viewed from the outside). (2) Whether, in frames without sills, metal dowels are required in the feet of the jambs.	Drawings and Bill items - CESMM class Z as appropriate.	

Clause	Description	Information to be provided	To be included in	Check
		(3) Which type of sill shall be supplied for inward-opening external door frames. (4) Whether garage door frames are to be assembled or supplied in sets for site assembly. (5) If internal doors frames or storey frames are to be supplied assembled. (6) If door stops for internal door frames are to be supplied otherwise than in bundles. (7) If preservative treatment is required before priming, the extent and nature of the treatment shall be stated.		
2.89 NfG (i)	"The required type and size of lintel should be described in the Contract."	Type of any lintel from: Prestressed concrete Reinforced concrete Aerated concrete Steel Timber. The size required.	Bill items - CESMM class Z.	
2.92 NfG (ii)	"Requirements for glass should be described in the Contract."	Type of any glass chosen from: Annealed flat glasses Clear float or polished plate Body tinted float or polished plate Surface modified tinted float Surface coated float Clear sheet Body tinted sheet Clear cast Body tinted cast Cast wired Polished wired Processed flat glasses Clear float toughened Sheet toughened Polished plate toughened Body tinted float toughened Surface modified tinted float toughened Cast toughened Cladding Insulated infill panels Laminated glasses Laminated safety Anti-bandit Bullet-resistant	Bill items - CESMM class Z.	

Clause	Description	Information to be provided	To be included in	Check
		Blast-resistant Solar control tinted interlayer Solar control reflective coating Laminated wired. Insulating glass units Thickness from those available depending on pane size.		
2.93 NfG (ii)	"Special requirements may be necessary for putty for use with double glazing."	Any special requirements for the putty.	Supplementary Clause.	
2.94 NfG (iii)	"The required type of priming paint should be described in the Contract."	Any type required from the tables in Clauses 2.94.5 and 2.94.6.	Bill items - CESMM class V.	
2.98 NfG (i)	"The required type, grade and thickness of board [for panelling] should be described in the Contract."	Any type from the table in Clause 2.98.1. Thickness from those available in the appropriate British Standard. Grade chosen from: BS 1142 Standard hardboard SHA, SHB, SHC Tempered hardboard THE, THN High density mediumboard HME, HMN Low density mediumboard LME, LMN Medium density fibreboard MDE Moisture resistant medium density fibreboard MDEMR Softboard SBN Impregnated softboard SBI, SBS BS 1230: Part 1 Gypsum wallboard Gypsum base wallboard Gypsum moisture resistant wallboard Gypsum moisture repellent wallboard Gypsum wallboard F Gypsum baseboard Gypsum baseboard F	Bill items - CESMM class Z.	

Clause	Description	Information to be provided	To be included in	Check
		BS 3837: Part 1 SD: Standard duty HD: High duty EHD: Extra high duty UHD: Ultra high duty ISD: Impact sound duty BS 4022 Specify by thickness only. BS 4841: Part 1 Thermal Code Conductivity W(m.K) 0.015 15 0.016 16 0.017 17 0.018 18 etc. to 0.032 32 BS 4841: Part 2 Specify by thickness only. BS 4965 Types H/1, H/2, H/S, HN, HN/S For use in heavy duty applications. Types LH, LH/S, LN, LN/S For use in light duty applications. BS 7331 DH/C1A High wear resistance surface on general purpose substrate. DH/C3 High wear resistance surface on improved moisture resistance substrate. DH/C5 High wear resistance surface on improved moisture resistance and enhanced mechanical property substrate. DG/C1 General purpose surface on general purpose substrate. DG/C3 General purpose surface on improved moisture resistance substrate. DG/C5 General purpose surface on improved moisture resistance and enhanced mechanical property substrate. BS 5669: Part 4 T1 - for internal use in dry conditions T2 - for internal or external use in the presence of moisture.		

Clause	Description	Information to be provided	To be included in	Check
2.99 NfG (i)	"In addition to the relevant Part of BS 6431 the type, size, thickness and colour of [wall] tiles should be described in the Contract."	Any type from: Extruded (shaping A) Split tiles (spaltplatten) Quarry Dust pressed (shaping B) Cast (shaping C) Size on a M=100 mm module using 2M, 3M and 5M. Thickness from those available in the appropriate part of BS 6431. Colour required.	Bill items - CESMM class Z.	
2.100 NfG (i)	"Facial sizes, thickness, colour and, in the case of floor quarries, category, [of floor tiles] should be described in the Contract."	Sizes and thickness from: BS 6431 Size on a M = 100mm module using 2M, 3M and 5M. Thickness as available. BS 2592 300mm x 300mm 250mm x 250mm Thickness 2.5mm or 3.0mm BS 3260 300mm x 300mm 225mm x 225mm Thickness 1.6mm, 2.0mm, 2.5mm, 3.0mm or 3.2mm BS 3261: Part 1 225mm x 225mm 250mm x 250mm 300mm x 300mm Thickness 1.5mm, 2.0mm, 2.5mm or 3.0mm. BS 4131 150mm x 150mm x 15mm 200mm x 200mm x 20mm 225mm x 225mm x 20mm 300mm x 300mm x 30mm 400mm x 400mm x 35mm 500mm x 500mm x 40mm Colour as required. Appropriate category of use for quarry tiles.	Bill items - CESMM class Z.	
2.101 NfG (i)	"Lower grades [of mastic asphalt for flooring] may be appropriate in other circumstances" (i.e. not loading sheds and heavy duty factory floors).	Any alternative grade and the flooring work in which it is to be used chosen as follows: Grade I - special hard flooring, e.g. Offices Grade II - light duty flooring, e.g. light factory floors. Grade III - medium duty flooring, e.g. floors or passageways subject to heavy foot traffic.	Supplementary Clause.	

Clause	Description	Information to be provided	To be included in	Check

2.102 NfG (i)	"The required type, grade, category, classification, size, group or colour of roof covering material should be described in the Contract."	Any type from table in Clause 2.102.1.
		Grade, category, size, group or colour from:
		BS 402: Part 1
		Size: 265 mm x 165 mm
		Hand made or machine made.
		BS 473, 550
		Group A Double-lap
		(non-interlocking)
		Size: 287mm x 165mm
		       457mm x 330mm
		Group B Single-lap (interlocking)
		Size: 381mm x 229mm
		       413mm x 330mm
		       420mm x 330mm
		       430mm x 380mm
		BS 680: Part 2
		Graded or ungraded.
		Size range: 225mm x 150mm to 610mm x 355mm
		BS 690: Part 4
		Fully compressed:
		Size: 600mm x 350mm
		       600mm x 300mm
		       500mm x 250mm
		Semi-compressed:
		Size: 600mm x 300mm
		BS 690: Part 5
		Profile class A - Pitched roofing and cladding.
		Profile class B - Cladding only.
		Profile asymmetrical or symmetrical.
		BS 747
		Class from:
		1: Bitumen felts (fibre base)
		2: Bitumen felts (asbestos base)
		3: Bitumen felts (glass fibre base)
		4: Sheathing felts and hair felts
		5: Bitumen felts (polyester base) with oxidized bitumen coating.
			Bill items - CESMM class Z.	

2.104 NfG (i)	"Any requirements for a different material, or thickness of sheet [for flashing] should be described in the Contract."	Any different material e.g. copper, or thickness of lead required.	Supplementary Clause. Bill items - CESMM class U.	
2.105 NfG (i)	"The type, class and grade of bricks and blocks should be described in the Contract."	Any type from: Clay Precast concrete Masonry units Calcium silicate.	Bill items - CESMM class U.	

Clause	Description	Information to be provided	To be included in	Check

		Class or grade from:
		BS 3921
		Class:
		Engineering A
		Engineering B
		Damp-proof course 1
		Damp-proof course 2
		Other
		Grade:
		FL, FN, ML, MN, OL, ON
		F = frost resistant
		M = moderately frost resistant
		O = not frost resistant
		L = low soluble salt content
		N = normal soluble salt
		    content
		BS 6073: Parts 1 and 2
		Class:
		Solid
		Cellular
		Hollow
		Perforated (brick)
		BS 187
		Class Compressive strength
		          not less than (N/mm^2)
		Loadbearing
		or facing
		7 48.5
		6 41.5
		5 34.5
		4 27.5
		3 20.5
		Facing or
		common
		2		

2.105 NfG (iii)	"Particular requirements for airbricks and gratings from the options listed in Appendix A of BS 493 should be described in the Contract."	Any requirements as to: (a) Class of units i.e. 1 or 2 (b) Co-ordinated size of units. (c) Design i.e. circular, square or rectangular hole or louvre. (d) Material in which units are to be made. (e) Whether units are to be self coloured or otherwise. (f) Whether any screening is required for Class 2 units. (g) Whether a certificate of compliance is required.	Supplementary Clause and/or Bill items - CESMM class U..	
2.108 NfG (i)	"Fittings and dimensions for [field] gates should be described in the Contract."	Dimensions: Timber gates: Width: 2.4m, 2.7m, 3m, 3.3m, 3.6m, 4.2m.	Bill items - CESMM class X and Drawings.	

Clause	Description	Information to be provided	To be included in	Check
		Height 1.1m. Steel gates: Width: Heavy duty: 2.4m, 3.0m, 3.6m, 4.5m. Light duty: 2.4m, 3.0m, 3.6m Height: 1.1m. Fittings from: Hinges Headstraps Fastenings. Timber, concrete or steel posts.		
2.111 NfG (i)	"The required size and type of [natural stone] setts should be described in the Contract."	Size (mm): Width x depth x length 100 x 100 x 100 75 x 125 75 x 150 100 x 100 all 150 to 250 100 x 125 100 x 150 Type by igneous rock required e.g. granite.	Bill items - CESMM class R	
2.112 NfG (i)	"The type, constituent material and colour of cast stone should be described in the Contract."	Grade A or B. Colour as required. Materials as required.	Bill items - CESMM class U.	
2.113 NfG (i)	"The required type of cement for cast coping units should be described in the Contract."	Type of cement required from tables in Clause 2.15.1.	Bill items - CESMM class H8.	
2.113.1	"Slate coping units shall be Type B unless otherwise described in the Contract."	That a Type A slate coping unit is required (in areas of high air pollution).	Bill items - CESMM class G6.	
2.115.1	"Unless otherwise described in the Contract [precast concrete] flags shall be 50 mm thick."	Any alternative thickness required.	Bill item - CESMM class R7.	
2.125 NfG (i)	"Fuel-resistant types of sealants to BS 2499 or BS 5212: Part 1 may be required where concrete surfaces are subject to regular fuel spillage."	Any requirement for fuel-resistant sealants.	Supplementary Clause. Bill items - CESMM class G6.	

Appendix 3 - Supplementary guidance for Section 3 - Excavation, backfilling and restoration

Clause	Description	Information to be provided	To be included in	Check
3.1 NfG (ii)	"CESMM requires a definition of 'rock' to be given, where required, in the Preamble to the Bill of Quantities."	Any definition of 'rock'.	Preamble to Bill of Quantities.	
3.1.7	"Trenches for pipes carrying water under pressure shall, except where otherwise described in the Contract, be excavated to a sufficient depth to ensure a minimum cover of 900 mm to the top of the pipes."	Any greater or lesser minimum cover required.	Drawings.	
3.1 NfG (iv)	"Any special requirements for Site clearance or for the disposal of excavated materials should be described in the Contract."	Any special requirements for clearance of the Site or for disposal of excavated materials.	Supplementary Clause.	
3.1 NfG (v)	"The Contract should describe the extent of any excavations where battered sides will be permitted. A detail of the allowable cross-section should be given."	Any extent of the excavations that may be battered. The allowable cross-section.	Drawings. Drawings.	
3.1 NfG (vii)	"CESMM provides for the measurement of probing ahead and temporary support in tunnels, items should be billed for these."	Length of any forward probing to be provided. Type of any temporary support required chosen from: Steel arches Timber supports Lagging Sprayed concrete Mesh or link. Quality of temporary support.	Bill items - CESMM class T8	
3.1.9	"It shall be the responsibility of the Contractor to decide the need for, and to undertake, any ground investigation ahead of the face of any tunnel, heading or shaft, additional to that described in the Contract."	The maximum length of any probing ahead for which the Employer will be responsible.	Bill items - CESMM class T8	
3.3.2	"Topsoil shall be removed from the areas prescribed in the Contract and, where required for re-use, shall be stock-piled separately and kept free from weeds."	Any areas from which topsoil is to be removed.	Drawings.	

Clause	Description	Information to be provided	To be included in	Check
3.3 NfG (i)	"It is advisable to make an assessment of soil stacking requirements in cases where topsoil quality is important, and to provide accordingly in the Contract."	Any areas on which the Contractor may stack topsoil.	Drawings.	
3.4.1	"The Contractor shall not allow water to lie in any part of the Works unless required to do so under the Contract."	Any requirement on the Contractor to allow water to lie, e.g. where the design of the Works requires this.	Drawings and Supplementary Clause.	
3.7 NfG (i)	"Any special requirements for backfilling around mains and services should be described in the Contract."	Any backfilling requirements specified by the owner of the main or service.	Supplementary Clause.	
3.7 NfG (ii)	"Any particular requirements for the materials to be used for backfilling should be described in the Contract."	Any special materials to be used for backfilling.	Supplementary Clause.	
3.8 NfG (i)	"Any particular requirements for the reinstatement method, materials and depths of layers should be described in the Contract."	Any particular methods, materials and depths of layers required chosen from those available in Appendices A3 to A8 of the HAUC Specification. The type of street, e.g. Type 1, 2, 3, or 4. The composition of any existing street, e.g. flexible, composite.	Bill items - CESMM class K7.	
3.9 NfG (i)	"Where the HAUC Specification is inappropriate, the reinstatement should be described in the Contract."	Any reinstatement required.	Bill items - CESMM class K7.	
3.10 NfG (i)	"Any special grass seed mixtures required, differing from those specified in Clause 2.6, should be described in the Contract."	Any special grass mixtures required, e.g. where specified by the landowner/occupier.	Supplementary Clause.	
3.10 NfG (ii)	"Any requirements to apply fertiliser should be described in the Contract."	The type of any fertiliser to be applied chosen from the table in Clause 2.7.1 or as specified by the landowner/occupier. The rate of application. The season(s) when it should be applied.	Supplementary Clause.	

Clause	Description	Information to be provided	To be included in	Check
3.10 NfG (iii)	"Any requirements of grass cutting and weed killing should be described in the Contract."	The number and seasons of any cuts. The type and rate of application of any weedkiller and when it should be applied.	Supplementary Clause.	
3.12 NfG (i)	"Any special requirements necessary to facilitate the restoration of land drainage should be described in the Contract."	Details of any special requirements for restoration of the land drainage,. e.g. those agreed with the owner of the land.	Drawings and Supplementary Clause.	
3.13 NfG (i)	"A more thorough specification [for filling above ground] may be necessary in other cases." (other than where the filling performs no specific load-bearing or structural role).	Specification of any filling above ground appropriate to the load-bearing or structural role that the filled ground is to perform, e.g. where a road or other structure will bear on the filled ground. The specification may include the use of materials other than excavated material, e.g. conditioned pulverised-fuel ash in accordance with Clause 2.14.3.	Supplementary Clause.	
3.14 NfG (i)	"It may be necessary for the Contract to describe safe values for vibrational amplitude and peak particle velocity" (where blasting is used).	Any maximum safe values for vibrational amplitude and peak particle velocity that are to apply, e.g. where adjacent structures are at risk or there is a public safety concern.	Supplementary Clause.	

Appendix 4 - Supplementary guidance for Section 4 - Concrete and formwork

Clause	Description	Information to be provided	To be included in	Check
4.2 NfG (i)	"Any restrictions on the use of ready-mixed concrete in the Works should be described in the Contract."	Any restrictions that are to apply.	Supplementary Clause.	
4.2 NfG (iii)	"Any requirements for information concerning the taking of test cubes or slump or other workability factor determinations, should be described in the Contract."	Any information that the Contractor is to obtain from the Ready-mixed concrete supplier regarding the taking of test cubes or slump or other workability factor determinations.	Supplementary Clause.	
4.2 NfG (v)	"Any restrictions on the use of admixtures in the Works should be described in the Contract (see Clause 5.3 of BS 5328: Part 2)."	Any type(s) of prohibited admixtures.	Supplementary Clause.	
4.3 NfG (i)	"If the rates given in the table in Clause 4.3.6 are not appropriate then the frequency of sampling should be described in the Contract."	Any alternative sampling rates of concrete for the determination of its compressive strength and the places in the Works where these alternative rates are to apply.	Supplementary Clause.	
4.3 NfG (ii)	"The characteristic compressive strength described in the Contract."	Any required characteristic strength.	Bill items - CESMM classes F1, F2, F3 and F4.	
4.3 NfG (iii)	"Where it is important that concrete should attain its maximum impermeability within 6 months of placing, a maximum free water/cementitious ratio less than 0.6 will be required, and should be described in the Contract."	Any requirement that the concrete should have a maximum free water/cementitious ratio of less than 0.6 for concrete that is not to retain an aqueous liquid (where the maximum allowable water/cementitious ratio is 0.55 in any case). Any particular concrete to which the requirement applies.	Supplementary Clause and Bill items - CESMM classes F1, F2, F3 and F4.	
4.3 NfG (iv)	"The exposure condition [for concrete] should be described in the Contract."	The exposure condition from the table in Clause 4.3.3. BS 8110: Part 1 contains the following descriptions of these exposure conditions and the additional 'Extreme' condition. Mild - Concrete surfaces protected against weather or aggressive conditions.	Bill items - CESMM classes F1, F2, F3 and F4.	

Clause	Description	Information to be provided	To be included in	Check
		Moderate - Concrete surfaces sheltered from severe rain or freezing whilst wet. Concrete subject to condensation. Concrete surfaces continuously under water. Concrete in contact with non-aggressive soil. Severe - Concrete surfaces exposed to severe rain, alternate wetting and drying or occasional freezing or severe condensation. Very severe - Concrete surfaces exposed to sea water spray, de - icing salts (directly or indirectly), corrosive fumes or severe freezing conditions whilst wet. Extreme - Concrete surfaces exposed to abrasive action, e.g. sea water carrying solids or flowing water with pH = < 4.5 or machinery or vehicles. If extreme exposure conditions are to be included additional information from Table 3.4 of BS 8110: Part 1 for these conditions will need to be added to the Contract.	Supplementary Clause.	
4.3 NfG (v)	"Specific precautions to minimise unacceptable damage from alkali-silica reaction should be described in the Contract."	Any precautions from those described in Clause 4.2.4 of BS 5328: Part 1 that are to apply.	Supplementary Clause.	
4.3.3	"Unless otherwise described in the Contract, the cementitious content of concrete shall not exceed 400 kg/m^3 or 450 kg/m^3 where pfa forms a cementitious component and the structure is designed to retain an aqueous liquid."	Any alternative maximum cementitious content of the concrete in kg/m^3 and the particular concretes to which the alternative maximum content will apply, e.g. very high strength concrete.	Supplementary Clause.	
4.4 NfG (i)	"Where it is not practicable to carry out full scale trials [of concrete mixes], special reference should be made in the Contract to laboratory scale mixes."	Any requirement for and specification of the laboratory scale trials of concrete mixes.	Supplementary Clause.	
4.4 NfG (ii)	"It may be necessary to specify water absorption tests for structures designed to retain an aqueous liquid."	Any requirement for water absorption tests of the concrete and any specification of the test method to be employed.	Supplementary Clause.	

Clause	Description	Information to be provided	To be included in	Check
4.12 NfG (i)	"Any requirements for placing concrete in special sequence, e.g. by alternate bay construction, should be described in the Contract."	Any special sequence of placing of the concrete required.	Supplementary Clause and Drawings.	
4.17 NfG (ii)	"The positioning and detailing of movement joints should be described in the Contract."	The positions and details of any movements joints required.	Drawings.	
4.17 NfG (iii)	"Any special conditions relating to the re-use of forms, insofar as the materials of construction and repairs between uses may affect the colour and surface finish of exposed surfaces, should be described in the Contract."	Any special conditions that are to apply to the re-use of forms.	Supplementary Clause.	
4.17 NfG (iv)	"Any special requirements regarding chamfers to internal and external angles [of concrete] should be described in the Contract."	Details of any chamfers to internal and external angles of any concrete members.	Drawings and Bill items - CESMM classes G186, G286, G386 and G486.	
4.19 NfG (iii)	"Any requirement for the control of thermal cracking [of concrete] should be described in the Contract."	Any physical requirements, e.g. the use of rebates or special waterstops to direct thermal cracking.	Drawings and Bill items - CESMM class G.	
4.20 NfG (i)	"Any requirement for top formwork at slopes flatter than 30° to the horizontal should be described in the Contract."	Any concrete surfaces between 0° and 30° for which formwork is to be provided. Formwork inclined between 0° and 5° is classed as horizontal and between 5° and 30° as sloping in the CESMM.	Drawings and Bill items - CESMM classes G11 and G12.	
4.23 NfG (i)	"Any protection for steel left projecting [from concrete] should be described in the Contract."	Any protection to be applied to the exposed steel, e.g. where structures are to be extended at a future date.	Supplementary Clause and Drawings.	
4.24.1	"Laps and joints in reinforcement shall be made at the positions described in the Contract or as agreed by the Engineer."	Any positions where laps and joints in reinforcement are to be made.	Drawings.	
4.25.1	"Reinforcement shall not be welded on Site except where described in or permitted under the Contract."	Any particular reinforcement that is required to be welded. Any general permission for the welding of reinforcement and the particular classes or types of reinforcement to which the permission applies.	Drawings. Supplementary Clause.	

Clause	Description	Information to be provided	To be included in	Check
4.27.1	"Except where construction joints in concrete are described in the Contract."	Any required positions and details of the construction joints.	Drawings.	
4.27.4	"The top surface of each lift of concrete shall be straight and level unless described otherwise in the Contract."	Any required deviation from straightness and level required of the top surface of the concrete lift.	Drawings.	
4.28 NfG (i)	"Any other required finish [to concrete surfaces produced without formwork] should be described in the Contract."	Any alternative surface finish required, e.g. exposure of the aggregates by use of a retarder and brushing.	Supplementary Clause.	
4.29 NfG (i)	"If test panels [of concrete finishes produced with formwork] are required, these should be described in the Contract."	A description of any test panels required including any requirements for their retention as standards for comparison when deciding the acceptance of production surfaces.	Drawings and Supplementary Clause.	
4.33 NfG (i)	"Where more stringent tolerances [for concrete surfaces] are required, these should be described in the Contract."	Any alternative tolerances required.	Supplementary Clause.	

Appendix 5 - Supplementary guidance for Section 5 - Construction of pipelines, tunnels and ancillary works

Clause	Description	Information to be provided	To be included in	Check
5.1.6	"Where pipeline marker tape is specified [to be laid]."	Any requirement to lay marker tape with pipelines and any particular pipelines to which the requirement applies.	Supplementary Clause	
5.2 NfG (i)	"When puddled clay stanks are required, these should be described in the Contract."	Any requirement to provide and any details of the puddled clay stanks.	Supplementary Clause.	
5.5.2	"Headings shall be driven from shaft to shaft or in such other lengths as may be described in the Contract."	Any alternative driven length required and any headings to which this is to apply.	Bill items - CESMM class L21.	
5.5.4	"Where grouting of headings is described in the Contract."	Any requirement to grout headings.	Supplementary Clause.	
5.6 NfG (i)	"Thrust blocks should either be described in the Contract or constructed in accordance with the Engineer's instructions on Site."	The dimensions and positions of any thrust blocks. The volume of any concrete required in thrust blocks.	Drawings. Bill items - CESMM class L7.	
5.7 NfG (ii)	"Any special requirements for filling the [pipe] joint annulus should be described in the Contract."	Any special requirements, e.g. filling with a specified flexible compound.	Supplementary Clause.	
5.8 NfG (iii)	"Any requirement for weld tests [of joints in plastics pipes] should be described in the Contract."	The requirements for any weld tests and the number of tests to be carried out.	Bill items - CESMM class A26.	
5.9 NfG (i)	"Where the Contractor is not required to provide nuts, bolts, washers and/or jointing gaskets, this should be described in the Contract."	A declaration that any nuts, bolts, washers and/or jointing gaskets are free issue to the Contractor.	Bill items - CESMM classes I and J.	
5.9 NfG (ii)	"Any special requirements for the type of flange gasket should be described in the Contract. See also Clause 2.48."	Any alternative to the inside - bolt - circle type gasket that is required, e.g. full face gaskets.	Bill items - CESMM classes I and J.	
5.10 NfG (i)	"Any required jointing material (mastic or cement mortar) [for ogee joints] should be described in the Contract."	Any jointing material required, e.g. mastic or cement mortar. The Class of mortar (M1-M4) from the table in Clause 2.20.1 if mortar is required.	Bill items - CESMM classes I and J.	

Clause	Description	Information to be provided	To be included in	Check
5.11 NfG (ii)	"The types of welded joint [for steel pipelines] should be described in the Contract."	The type of any welding of joints required chosen from: Manual metal-arc Submerged-arc MIG/MAG TIG CO_2 Non-shielded Hyperbaric.	Bill items - CESMM classes I and J.	
5.11 NfG (iii)	"The frequency and type of testing [of welds in steel pipelines] should be described in the Contract."	The frequency and type, (e.g. non-destructive, destructive,) of any tests required.	Bill items - CESMM class A26.	
5.14 NfG (ii)	"Any limitation on the type of external or internal protection required [of ferrous pipes, joints and fittings] should be described in the Contract."	Any limitations on the Contractor regarding the options in Clauses 5.14.2 and 5.14.3, e.g. the exclusion of heat shrunk sleeves in confined spaces.	Supplementary Clause.	
5.14 NfG (iii)	"The type of external protection required [to ferrous pipes, joints and fittings] should be described in the Contract."	The type of any external protection required chosen from P1 to P7.	Bill items - CESMM classes I and J.	
5.14 NfG (v)	"Any requirements for the design of the cathodic protection [of ferrous pipes, joints and fittings] should be described in the Contract."	Any design requirements, including the design life, for the cathodic protection.	Supplementary Clause.	
5.14.3	"P7 - Painting the external surface [of ferrous pipes, joints and fittings] as described in the Contract."	The specification of any painting required.	Supplementary Clause.	
5.16 NfG (i)	"The type of jointing material [for precast concrete manhole sections] should be described in the Contract."	The type of any jointing material required.	Bill items - CESMM classes K15 and K16.	
5.19 NfG (i)	"The benching material and surface finish [for manhole inverts and benchings] should be described in the Contract."	Any benching material required chosen from: In-situ concrete High strength concrete topping (granolithic finish) Other material. The required surface finish chosen from: Steel Trowel Fair Worked.	Bill items - CESMM class K1.	

Clause	Description	Information to be provided	To be included in	Check
5.22 1	"Manhole frames shall be set to the required level on Class B engineering brickwork, or on precast concrete cover seating rings, as described in the Contract."	Any seating method required chosen from: Class B Engineering brickwork. Precast concrete cover seating rings.	Bill items - CESMM class K.	
5.22 NfG (i)	"If bedding of [manhole cover] frames on epoxy resin or haunching in concrete (instead of mortar) is required, this should be described in the Contract."	Any specification for epoxy resin. Any requirement to bed the manhole cover frames on epoxy resin and/or the requirement to haunch frames in concrete (including the class of concrete required).	Supplementary Clause in Section 2. Bill items - CESMM class K.	
5.24 NfG (i)	"The material required for filling [sewers and manholes to be abandoned] should be described in the Contract."	Any material to be used chosen from: Grout (including the class G1 - G6 from the table in Clause 2.19.1) Pfa Sand Pea gravel Bentonite Other material.	Bill items - CESMM class C5.	
5.24 NfG (ii)	"Any requirement for clearing sewers prior to filling should be described in the Contract."	Any requirement to clear sewers prior to filling.	Supplementary Clause.	
5.24.2	"The shafts of manholes on abandoned sewers shall be broken down to a level 1m below finished ground level and the remaining void filled as described in the Contract."	Any materials to be used and any performance required of the filling operation.	Supplementary Clause and Bill items - CESMM class E6.	
5.25.8	"Unless otherwise required by the Contract joint packing material designed to distribute the jacking load evenly shall be inserted at and between the pipe ends and at intermediate jacking stations."	Any alternative requirements for the insertion of joint packing material.	Supplementary Clause.	
5.26 NfG (i)	"Any special requirements relating to protection [in shafts] should be described in the Contract."	Any special requirements for the protection of ladders, landings, supporting structures and people in shafts	Supplementary Clause.	
5.26 NfG (ii)	"Special clauses will be required for other types of shaft sinking."	Any alternative specification for shaft sinking, e.g. ground freezing.	Supplementary Clause.	

Clause	Description	Information to be provided	To be included in	Check
5.27 NfG (ii)	"The Contract should describe any limitations which the design of the tunnel or shaft will impose on temporary openings."	Any limitations which the design will impose.	Supplementary Clause.	
5.29 NfG (i)	"Requirements for any circumferential pre-stress [on unbolted concrete tunnel segments] should be described in the Contract."	Any requirement for and the degree of circumferential pre-stress.	Supplementary Clause.	
5.30 NfG (i)	"Any requirement relating to rolling of [concrete tunnel and shaft lining] segments should be described in the Contract."	Any requirement relating to the rolling of segments.	Supplementary Clause.	
5.30 NfG (ii)	"Any requirement for bituminous jointing strips in circumferential joints [of bolted concrete segmental linings] should be described in the Contract."	Any requirement for and the details of the bituminous jointing strips.	Bill items - CESMM classes T5, T6 and T7.	
5.31 NfG (i)	"Any requirements for high pressure grouting [of segmental shaft and tunnel linings] should be described in the Contract."	Any requirements for segmental shaft and tunnel linings to grouted under high pressure. The class of any grout to be used chosen from class G1-G6 in the table in Clause 2.19.1.	Bill items - CESMM class T8.	
5.31 NfG (ii)	"Any locations where it is required to grout [segmental shaft and tunnel linings] more frequently than once per shift should be described in the Contract."	Any required locations and the number of times per shift that any grouting is to be carried out.	Drawings and Supplementary Clause.	
5.32 NfG (i)	"Material to be used for caulking [segment joints in tunnels and shafts] should be described in the Contract."	The material to be used for caulking any segment joints.	Bill items - CESMM classes T5, T6 and T7.	
5.32.2	"Caulking of circumferential and longitudinal joints shall be bonded to form a homogeneous and continuous mass consolidated to fill the recess up to the inner surface of the segment or to the depths described in the Contract."	The depth of any required rebate.	Bill items - CESMM classes T5, T6 and T7.	

Appendix 6 - Supplementary guidance for Section 6 - Building works

Clause	Description	Information to be provided	To be included in	Check
6.1 NfG (ii)	"Any requirement for rendering of manholes and chambers should be described in the Contract."	Any requirement to render the manholes and chambers and the thickness of the rendering.	Drawings and Bill items - CESMM classes K1 and K2.	
6.1 NfG (iii)	"The bond [for brickwork and blockwork] should be described in the Contract."	Any bond required chosen from: Brickwork: English Flemish English garden-wall Flemish garden-wall (Sussex garden-wall) Heading (header) Quetta Rat-trap Blockwork: Running (stretcher) Thin stretcher Off-centre running.	Drawings and Bill items - CESMM class U.	
6.1 NfG (iv)	"The required class of mortar and type of cement [for brickwork and blockwork] should be described in the Contract. See Clause 2.20."	The class of any mortar required (M1-M8) chosen from the table in Clause 2.20.1. For classes M1-M4 the type of cement to be used in the mortar chosen from the tables in Clause 2.15.1.	Drawings and Bill items - CESMM class U.	
6.2 NfG (i)	"The type of jointing and pointing [of brickwork and blockwork] should be described in the Contract."	The type of any jointing/pointing required chosen from: Flush Struck or weathered Bucket handle (keyed) Recessed.	Drawings and Bill items - CESMM class U.	
6.3 NfG (i)	"Where the filling or semi-filling of cavities [in cavity walls] with insulating material is required it should be described in the Contract."	Any particular insulating material required and its grade, e.g. expanded polystyrene boards or rigid urethane foam boards., and whether cavities are to be filled or semi-filled.	Drawings and Bill items - CESMM class U.	
6.7 NfG (i)	"Larger scale underpinning [in brickwork] should be described in the Contract and may require the services of a specialist contractor"	A description of any underpinning required and whether a specialist sub - contractor is to be employed.	Supplementary Clause and/or Drawings. Bill items - CESMM class A5 or U as appropriate.	
6.10 NfG (i)	"The type of scrim material [for plastering] should be described in the Contract."	Any scrim material to be used, e.g. jute scrim, cotton scrim or plasterboard joint tape.	Bill items - CESMM class Z4.	

Clause	Description	Information to be provided	To be included in	Check
6.10 NfG (ii)	"If joints [in plasterwork] are to be cut or covered as an alternative to scrim this should be described in the Contract."	Any alternative method of cutting or covering required.	Bill items - CESMM class Z4.	
6.14 NfG (i)	"The type of [concrete floor] finish from BS 8204: Part 2 should be described in the Contract."	The class of any finish required chosen from: Special - where severe abrasion and impact is expected in very heavy duty engineering workshops. AR1 - where very high abrasion, steel wheel traffic and impact is expected in heavy duty industrial workshops, special commercial areas, etc.. AR2 - where high abrasion and steel or hard plastic wheel traffic is expected in medium duty industrial and commercial areas. AR3 - where moderate abrasion and rubber tyred traffic is expected in light duty industrial and commercial areas.	Bill items - CESMM class Z4.	
6.19.2	"Except where [carpentry and joinery] work is described in the Contract as being to finished sizes."	Any finished sizes of any carpentry and joinery work required.	Drawings and Bill items - CESMM class Z1.	
6.20 NfG (ii)	"End connection, baseplates and other design requirements [for structural steelwork] should be described in the Contract."	Details of any end connection, baseplates and other design requirements.	Drawings and Bill items - CESMM class M.	
6.20 NfG (iii)	"Where steelwork is to be galvanised it should be described in the Contract."	The requirement for any steelwork to be galvanised and the standard of any galvanising required e.g. BS 729.	Bill items - CESMM class M.	
6.22 NfG (i)	"Thickness of floor boarding should be described in the Contract."	Any required thickness.	Bill items - CESMM class Z1.	
6.22 NfG (ii)	"If chipboard is to be used instead of floor boarding this should be described in the Contract."	The requirement for the use of any chipboard.	Drawings and Bill items - CESMM class Z13.	
6.22.1	"Floor joists shall be trimmed as described in the Contract."	Any trimming required.	Drawings.	

Clause	Description	Information to be provided	To be included in	Check
6.27 NfG (i)	"The types and sizes of slate and tiles together with details of any laps, battens, fixings, beddings, underfelt and boarding should be described in the Contract."	Any required types, sizes and details. (See the entry against Clause 2.102 NfG (i)).	Drawings and Bill items - CESMM class Z4.	
6.31.1	"Mineral aggregates for flat roofs shall be applied to flat asphalt and bitumen felt roofs where so described in the Contract."	Any flat roofs to which the mineral aggregates are to be applied. The aggregate required chosen from: Hard limestone (but see Clause 2.103 NfG (ii)) Granite Gravel Calcined flint Calcite Felspar.	Drawings and Bill items - CESMM class Z4.	
6.31 NfG (i)	"If reflective paint is to be used as an alternative to mineral aggregates, it should be described in the Contract."	Any roofs where reflective paint is to be used and the type of paint to be used.	Drawings and Bill items - CESMM class Z4.	
6.32 NfG (i)	"Where heating and hot water systems are to be installed, reference should be made to BS 5449 and BS 6880: Parts 1 - 3."	The requirement that any hot water central heating systems should be installed to BS 5449 where these are included in the Works and/or the requirement that hot water heating systems are to be designed and installed to BS 6880 where these are included. Preliminary design information as follows: (a) Thermal characteristics of the building for calculation of heat requirements and possible improvements for energy conservation. (b) Fuel to be used. (c) Position of the boiler, bearing in mind access for maintenance, means of fuelling and provision of combustion air. (d) Type, location, dimensions, construction and suitability of chimney and flue terminal, where required. (e) Location and size of fuel storage and access thereto, where required. For solid fuel, ash removal and disposal will require consideration.	Drawings and Supplementary Clause. Bill item - CESMM class A4 or A5.	

Clause	Description	Information to be provided	To be included in	Check
		(f) Position of feed and expansion cistern for open systems or expansion vessel, filling point and pressure gauge for sealed systems. (g) Facilities for filling and draining the system. (h) Requirements for domestic hot water supply equipment, e.g. hot water storage cylinder, if required. (j) Temperatures required to be maintained and the manner in which the dwelling and system are to be used, bearing in mind ventilation and condensation. (k) Type and position of heat emitters. (l) System control of heating and hot water including frost protection. (m) Route and method of installing pipework. (n) The need for compliance with relevant Building Regulations, Gas Safety (Installation and Use) Regulations, Regulations for Electrical Installations, Water Bye - laws and BS Codes of Practice.		
6.33.1	"Where described in the Contract [the Contractor] shall provide and fix in position approved tube sleeves [to openings in walls, floors and ceilings]."	The requirement for and the positions where any tube sleeves are required.	Drawings and Bill items - CESMM class Z5.	
6.34.1	"Tolerance for building works, except where otherwise described in the Contract, shall not exceed the permissible deviations from levels and dimensions given in BS 5606."	Any alternative permissible deviations.	Supplementary Clause.	
AT.1	"Certain facts (e.g. the size of cables in the incoming supply) should be described in the Contract."	The factual information relative to any electrical installation.	Drawings and/or a Supplementary Clause.	

Appendix 7 - Supplementary guidance for Section 7 - Testing and disinfection

Clause	Description	Information to be provided	To be included in	Check
7.4 NfG (i)	"The type of test (air, water, visual or CCTV) [for non-pressure pipelines] should be described in the Contract"	The type of test required for each length of pipeline to be tested.	Bill items - CESMM class A26.	
7.5.2	"Unless otherwise specified, the length of [non-pressure] pipeline [under test] shall be accepted if the quantity of water added over a 30 minute period is less than 0.5 litre per lineal metre per metre of nominal bore."	Any alternative acceptable quantity of water added. The alternative period over which the water is to be added (if any).	Supplementary Clause.	
7.7 NfG (i)	"CCTV inspection should be described in the Contract if required."	Any requirement for CCTV inspection and the lengths and internal diameters of the pipelines to be inspected.	Bill items - CESMM classes Y13 and Y54.	
7.9 NfG (i)	"Where pipes are of MDPE, pre-stressed concrete, or other materials [except ductile iron, asbestos cement, GRP and PVC - U], special clauses will be necessary."	Any alternative specification for testing the pipeline.	Supplementary Clause.	
7.9 NfG (iii)	"This period [of standing under operating pressure] should be described in the Contract together with the design operating pressure."	The period any pipeline is to stand under operating pressure and the operating pressure required.	Bill items - CESMM class A26.	
7.9 NfG (iv)	"The test pressures [for pressure pipelines] should be described in the Contract."	Any required test pressures.	Bill items - CESMM class A26.	
7.10 NfG (i)	"The Contract should describe who provides swabs and temporary pipework, the type of swab and the maximum number of passes to be run at the Employer's expense."	Whether the Employer or the Contractor is to provide any swabs and temporary pipework. The type of swab and the maximum number of passes at the Employer's expense.	Supplementary Clause.	
7.14 NfG (i)	"The Contract should describe which of the two alternative tests [of service reservoir roofs] is required."	Whether lagooning or continuous hosing of any roof is required.	Bill items - CESMM class A26.	
7.15 NfG (i)	"This clause [for the disinfection of structures for potable water] will not apply if the Employer wishes to undertake disinfection."	Whether the Employer is to undertake disinfection of any structures.	Supplementary Clause.	

Clause	Description	Information to be provided	To be included in	Check
7.16 NfG (i)	"Grout strength requirements should be described in the Contract."	Any grout function chosen from the table in Clause 7.16.3.	Bill items - CESMM class A25.	
7.16.2	"The density [of grout] shall not differ from the value described in the Contract by more than 5%."	The density of any grout required.	Supplementary Clause in Section 5 and/or Section 9.	
7.16.2	"The workability [of grout] shall not differ by more than 125 mm for the 'Colcrete flow trough test' or 5 seconds for the 'Marsh cone test' with 10 mm orifice from the values described in the Contract."	Any required workability.	Supplementary Clause in Section 5 and/or Section 9.	
AT.1	"Testing of operational equipment installed by the Contractor should be described in item descriptions."	Requirements for the testing of any operational equipment.	Bill items - CESMM class A26.	
AT.2	"The Contract should describe who is responsible for providing water for each testing operation, the points of supply, quality and programmed rates of delivery and for the disposing of test water on completion, having regard to the pollution of watercourses. See Clause 1.14."	Whether the Employer or the Contractor is responsible for providing water for each particular testing operation. The quantity and rates of delivery of water for testing and the responsibility for disposal of the test water on completion. The points of supply of water.	Supplementary Clause. Drawings.	

Appendix 8 - Supplementary guidance for Section 8 - Roadworks

Clause	Description	Information to be provided	To be included in	Check
8.1 NfG (i)	"A cross-section of the carriageway construction, and the position and type of any joints, should be described in the Contract."	Any required carriageway cross-section and the position and type of joints.	Drawings.	
8.2 NfG (i)	"If a lean-mix concrete sub-base is required, this should be described in the Contract."	Whether any lean - mix concrete sub - base is required. The grade of any concrete required, e.g. a DTp Specified strength.	Drawings and Bill items - CESMM class R15.	
8.9 NfG (i)	"The positioning and detailing of movement joints [in concrete carriageways] should be described in the Contract."	The positioning and required details of any movement joints.	Drawings and Bill items - CESMM class R5.	
8.10.1	"Kerbs, edgings, channels and quadrants shall be laid on a layer of Class M1 mortar, either on the concrete carriageway or on a Grade C20 concrete foundation, as described in the Contract."	Whether any kerbs, edgings and quadrants are to be laid on the carriageway or on a separate concrete foundation.	Drawings and Bill items - CESMM class R6.	
8.10.1	"Kerbs, edgings, channels and quadrants shall be butt - jointed except where otherwise described in the Contract."	Any alternative jointing requirements for kerbs, edgings, channels and quadrants.	Drawings and Bill items - CESMM class R6.	
8.10 NfG (i)	"Details of the concrete bed and haunch [to kerbs and channels etc.] should be described in the Contract."	Details of any required concrete bed and haunch.	Drawings and Bill items - CESMM class R6.	
8.10.3	"Alignment of kerbs and channels shall not deviate from that described in the Contract by more than 10 mm with no lipping of visible faces."	Any required alignment.	Drawings.	
8.11 NfG (i)	"A cross-section of the footway construction should be described in the Contract."	The required cross - section of any footway(s).	Drawings.	
8.12.1	"Precast concrete flags shall be laid to the required falls on sub-base material as described in the Contract."	Any required falls. Any required sub - base material, e.g. sand.	Drawings. Bill items - CESMM class R78.	

Clause	Description	Information to be provided	To be included in	Check
8.13.1	"Finished surfaces at each stage of road construction shall not vary from the levels described in the Contract by more than the following permissible deviations."	The required levels of finished surface at each stage of any road construction.	Drawings.	
8.14.1	"Gullies shall be bedded and surrounded with Grade C20 concrete to the thickness described in the Contract."	The required thickness of any concrete bed and surround.	Drawings and Bill items - CESMM class K3.	

Appendix 9 - Supplementary guidance for Section 9 - Sewer and water main renovation

Clause	Description	Information to be provided	To be included in	Check
General Note	"Special Specification Clauses will normally be required to describe the particular renovation system required."	Description of any particular renovation system required.	Supplementary Clause.	
9.1 NfG (i) (see AT.14 of Section 1)	"Estimates of dry-weather and peak flows should be indicated in the Contract."	Estimates of the dry - weather and peak flows in any sewer to be renovated.	Supplementary Clause.	
9.1 NfG (iii)	"Where the Contractor will be permitted to operate valves and isolate flows, this should be described in the Contract."	Any permitted valve operations and flow isolations that the Contractor may undertake.	Supplementary Clause.	
9.2 NfG (i)	"Any requirement for a structural condition survey shall be described in the Contract."	The requirement for any structural condition survey and how this is to be undertaken, e.g. by CCTV.	Supplementary Clause and Bill items - CESMM classes Y13 and Y54.	
9.3 NfG (i)	"Where the Contractor will be permitted to operate valves and hydrants, this should be described in the Contract."	Any permitted valve and hydrant operations the Contractor may undertake.	Supplementary Clause.	
9.8 NfG (i)	"Any alternative [to 50 kN/m^2] maximum grout pressures should be described in the Contract."	Any alternative maximum grout pressure allowed.	Supplementary Clause.	
9.11 NfG (i)	"The format of the information required and any need for a CCTV survey should be described in the Contract."	The required information, the format in which it is required and whether a CCTV survey of any renovated sewer or water main is needed.	Supplementary Clause.	
9.11 NfG (ii)	"The number of samples [of renovated pipes] to be removed, and the length of the sample should be described in the Contract."	The number and length of any samples to be removed.	Bill items - CESMM class A26.	

REFERENCES

1.   "Reorganization of water and sewage services: Government proposals and arrangements for consultation" - DoE Circular 92/71, 2 December 1971. HMSO.

2.   "The future management of water in England and Wales" - Report of the Central Advisory Water Committee, April 1971. HMSO.

3.   "Water Act 1973" - Chapter 37. HMSO.

4.   "The new water industry management and structure" - Report of the Ogden Committee, June 1973. HMSO.

5.   "Item 9 of Note of a meeting of Directors of Operations held on 29 April 1974" - NWC, April 1974. Restricted circulation.

6.   "Standard specification for water and sewerage schemes" - Scottish Development Department, 1973. HMSO.

7.   "Conditions of Contract and Forms of Tender, Agreement and Bond for use in connection with Works of Civil Engineering Construction. Fifth Edition" - Joint Contracts Committee, June 1973. ICE/ACE/FCEC.

8.   "Clearing the critics' confusion" - Sir William Harris and David Gardham QC, New Civil Engineer magazine, 20 December 1973. Thomas Telford Limited.

9.   "Guidance Note 2A: Functions of the Engineer under the ICE Conditions of Contract" - ICE Conditions of Contract Standing Joint Committee, September 1977. ICE/ACE/FCEC.

10.   "ICE Conditions of Contract 6th Edition" - CCSJC, January 1991. Thomas Telford Limited.

11.   "Standard Method of Measurement of Civil Engineering Quantities - with Metrication Addendum" - ICE, 1974. ICE.

12.   "Civil Engineering Standard Method of Measurement" - ICE, January 1976. Thomas Telford Limited.

13.   "Notes for guidance on standard specification for water and sewerage schemes" - Scottish Development Department, 1973. HMSO.

14.   "Minute 77.251.1 of Legal & Parliamentary Group meeting on 6 December 1977" - NWC, December 1977. Restricted circulation.

15.   "Manual for Materials Information and Guidance Notes" - covering letter by WRc, 14 December 1982.

16.   "Piling: Model procedures and specifications" - ICE, 1978. Thomas Telford Ltd.

17.   "Well construction specification for the water industry" - WAA, May 1985.

18. "Civil Engineering Specification for the Water Industry (first edition) - Advisory Note No. 2" - NWC Review Committee, October 1981. NWC.

19. "Standards quality and international competitiveness" - DTI White Paper, July 1982. HMSO.

20. "The water industry's response to the White Paper on standards quality and international competitiveness" - NWC, 14 October 1982. Restricted circulation.

21. "Quality assurance" - Paper WAA/CE/85/40(amended) to WAA Chief Executives' Group meeting on 6 November 1985. Restricted circulation.

22. "Water industry quality assurance" - Report of the Quality Assurance Working Group, June 1986. Restricted circulation.

23. "Minute WAA/CE/86/52 of Chief Executives' Group meeting on 3 December 1986" - WAA, December 1986. Restricted circulation.

24. "Opinion of Mr Advocate General Darmon" - Delivered at the sitting of the Full Court in Case 45/87, 21 June 1988. English translation, Court of Justice of the European Communities.

25. "Asbestos-cement pressure pipes and joints" - ISO 160: 1980. ISO June 1980.

26. "Case 45/87: Commission of the European Communities, supported by The Kingdom of Spain, versus Ireland" - Judgement of the Court, 22 September 1988.   English translation, Court of Justice of the European Communities.

27. "Council Directive on the approximation of laws, regulations and administrative provisions of the Member States relating to construction products (89/106/EEC)" - done at Brussels, 21 December 1988.

28. "The Construction Products Regulations 1991" - S.I. 1991, No. 1620. HMSO.

29. "Comité Européen de Normalisation" (European Committee for Standardization).

30. "Comité European de Normalisation Electrotechnique" (European Committee for Electrotechnical Standardization).

31. "Interpretative documents of Council Directive 89/106/EEC" -Communication of the Commission, 28 February 1994, Notice No. 94/C.62/01. Official Journal of the European Communities, Information and Notices, C.62 - Volume 37.

32. "CEN/CENELEC Internal Regulations - Part 2: Common rules for standards work, April 1990 edition. CEN/CENELEC.

33. "Council Directive on the procurement procedures of entities operating in the water, energy, transport and telecommunications sectors (90/531/EEC)" - done at Brussels, 17 September 1990.

34. "The Utilities Supply and Works Contracts Regulations 1992" - S.I. 1992 No. 3279. HMSO.

35. "A standard for standards: Part 3. Guide to drafting and presentation of British Standards" - BS 0: Part 3: 1991. BSI.

36. Note 2B: Incorporation of Conditions of Contract into Contract documents" - ICE Conditions of Contract Standing Joint Committee, September 1977. ICE/ACE/FCEC.

37. "Draft Civil Engineering Specification for Water Authority Works" - NWC Specifications Working Group, March 1977. NWC.

38. "Civil Engineering Specification for the Water Industry" - NWC, July 1978. NWC.

39. "Civil Engineering Specification for the Water Industry: Advisory Note No.1" - NWC, October 1980. NWC Bulletin 40.

40. "Code of practice for safe use of explosives in the construction industry" - BS 5607: 1978. BSI.

41. "Civil Engineering Specification for the Water Industry - Advisory Note No.2" - NWC, October 1981. NWC.

42. "Civil Engineering Specification for the Water Industry: Second Edition" - WAA, July 1984. WRc.

43. "Water Act 1983". HMSO.

44. "Civil Engineering Standard Method of Measurement: Second Edition" - ICE, November 1985. Thomas Telford Limited.

45. "Civil Engineering Specification for the Water Industry: Second Edition - Advisory Note No.1" - WAA, August 1986. WRc.

46. "Structural use of concrete: Part 1. Code of practice for design and construction and Part 2. Code of practice for special circumstances" - BS 8110: Part 1 and Part 2: 1985. BSI.

47. "Civil Engineering Specification for the Water Industry: Third Edition" - WAA, May 1989. WRc.

48. "Specification for Highway Works" - DTp, December 1991. HMSO.

49. "Water Act 1989" - Chapter 15. HMSO.

50. "Civil Engineering Specification for the Water Industry: Third Edition - Advisory Note No.1" - WSA, October 1991. WRc.

51. "Civil Engineering Specification for the Water Industry (CESWI)" - Report WSA/WSMG/92/42 to WSA Water Services Management Group meeting on 6 May 1992. Restricted circulation.

52. "Civil Engineering Specification for the Water Industry: Second Edition - Advisory Note No.2" - WSA, June 1992. WRc.

53. "Civil Engineering Specification for the Water Industry: Fourth Edition" - WSA, October 1993. WRc.

54. "New Roads and Street Works Act 1991" - Chapter 22. HMSO.

55. "Civil Engineering Standard Method of Measurement: Third Edition" - ICE, 1991. Thomas Telford Services Limited.

56. "A model code of practice for the exercise of works powers by water and sewerage undertakers on land" - DoE, 24 July 1989. DoE.

57. "Traffic Signs Manual - Chapter 8: Traffic safety measures and signs for road works and temporary situations" - Department of Transport. HMSO.

58. "Transportable accommodation units: Part 1. Recommendations for design and construction " - BS 6767: Part 1: 1992. BSI.

59. "Water Industry Act 1991" - Chapter 56. HMSO.

60. "ICE Conditions of Contract Sixth Edition - Corrigenda" - CCSJC, July 1993. Thomas Telford Services Limited.

61. "Model Consultative Procedure for Pipeline Construction Involving Deep Excavation" - ERS M60, British Gas/WSA/WCA, January 1993. British Gas/WSA/WCA/FWR.

62. "Water Resources Act 1991" - Chapter 57. HMSO.

63. "Land Drainage Act 1991" - Chapter 59. HMSO.

64. "Operational guidelines for the protection of drinking water supplies" - WAA, September, 1988. WAA.

65. "The Work in Compressed Air Special Regulations 1958" - S.I. 61, 1958. HMSO.

66. "Medical code of practice for work in compressed air: Third edition 1982" - CIRIA Report R44, Reprinted with amendments 1992. CIRIA.

67. "Code of practice for safe use of explosives in the construction industry" - BS 5607: 1988. BSI.

68. "Item 78.25 of Note of a meeting of the Directors of Operations' Group held on 24 January 1978" - NWC, January 1978. Restricted circulation.

69. "Item 79.18 of Note of a meeting of the Directors of Operations' Group held on 27 February 1979" - NWC, February 1979. Restricted circulation.

70. "Item 80.28 of Note of a meeting of the Directors of Operations' Group held on 26 February 1980" - NWC, February 1980. Restricted circulation.

71. "The Water Supply (Water Quality) Regulations 1989" - S.I. 1989 No. 1147. HMSO.

72. "The Water Supply (Water Quality) (Amendment) Regulations 1989" - S.I. 1989 No. 1384. HMSO.

73. "Laying precast concrete pipes in trench" - Concrete Pipe Association Technical Bulletin, 1992. CPA.

74. "Concrete: Part 1. Guide to specifying concrete" - BS 5328: Part 1: 1991. BSI.

75. "Specification for aggregates from natural sources for concrete" - BS 882: 1992. BSI.

76. "Structural use of concrete: Part 1. Code of practice for design and construction; and Part 2. Code of practice for special circumstances" - BS 8110: Parts 1 and 2: 1985. BSI.

77. "Sulphate and acid resistance of concrete in the ground" - Digest 363 as corrected, July 1991. BRE.

78. "Specification for blast furnace slag cement for in situ lining of water mains" - WIs No. 4-13-01, Issue 1, March 1991. WRc.

79. "Specification for virtified clay pipes, fittings and ducts, also flexible mechanical joints for use solely with surface water pipes and fittings" - BS 65: 1991. BSI.

80. "Vitrified clay pipes and fittings and pipe joints for drains and sewers" - BS EN 295. BSI.

81. "Precast concrete pipes and ancillary concrete products: Part 100. Specification for unreinforced and reinforced pipes and fittings with flexible joints" - BS 5911: Part 100: 1988. BSI.

82. "Precast concrete pipes and ancillary concrete products: Part 110. Specification for ogee pipes and fittings (including perforated)" - BS 5911: Part 110: 1992. BSI.

83. "Precast concrete pipes and ancillary concrete products: Part 120. Specification for reinforced jacking pipes with flexible joints" - BS 5911: Part 120: 1989. BSI.

84. "Concrete pipes for jacking: Smaller diameters (microtunnel) and unreinforced pipes (Reference BS 5911: Part 120)" - PJA/CPA Technical Bulletin, Issue 1, August 1993. PJA/CPA.

85. "Specification for Class arc welding of carbon steel pipework for carrying fluids" - BS 2971: 1991. BSI.

86. "Specification for welding of steel pipelines on land and offshore" - BS 4515: 1984. BSI.

87. "Specification for arc welding of carbon and carbon manganese steels" - BS 5135: 1984. BSI.

88. "Specification for steel pipes, joints and specials for water and sewage" - BS 534: 1990. BSI.

89. "Specification for carbon steel pipes and tubes with specified room temperature properties for pressure purposes" - BS 3601: 1987. BSI.

90. "Specification for polymeric anti-corrosion (barrier) coatings" - WIs No. 4-52-01, Issue 1, December 1992. WRc.

91. "The use of polymeric anti-corrosion (barrier) coatings" - IGN No. 4-52-02, Issue 1, January 1993. WRc.

92. "Specification for unplasticized polyvinyl chloride (PVC-U) pressure pipes for cold potable water" - BS 3505: 1986. BSI.

93. "Specification for blue unplasticized PVC pressure pipes, integral joints and post-formed bends for cold potable water (underground use)" - WIs No. 4-31-06, Issue 1, January 1990. WRc.

94. "Specification for mechanical fittings and joints including flanges for polyethylene pipes for the conveyance of cold potable water for the size range 90 to 1000 inclusive made of metal or plastics or a combination of both" - WIs No. 4-24-01, Issue 1, April 1991. WRc.

95. "Specification for polyethylene electrofusion couplers and fittings for cold potable water supply for nominal sizes up to and including 180" - WIs No. 4-32-06, Issue 1, September 1989. WRc.

96. "Specification for black polyethylene pressure pipes for potable water above ground or sewerage (nominal sizes 90 to 1000)" - WIs No. 4-32-09, Issue 1, June 1991. WRc.

97. "Specification for blue higher performance polyethylene, HPPE/PE 100, pressure pipes, nominal size 90 to 1000, for underground or protected use for the conveyance of water intended for human consumption" - WIs No. 4-32-13, Issue 1, March 1993. WRc.

98. "Specification for end load resistant mechanical joints and compression fittings made principally of thermoplastics for use with polyethylene pipes of nominal size ó63 with outside diameters to BS 5556 (metric)" - WIs No. 4-32-11, Issue 1, March 1990. WRc.

99. "Capillary and compression tube fittings of copper and copper alloy: Part 5. Specification for compression fittings for polyethylene pipes with outside diameters to BS 5556" - BS 864: Part 5: 1990. BSI.

100. "Specification for underground stop valves, including spherical valves, for potable water services for nominal sizes up to and including 63 and nominal pressures of 10 bar minimum and made principally of metal or thermoplastics" - WIs No. 4-23-04, Issue 1, March 1991. WRc.

101. "Specification for ferrules (tapping tees) and ferrule straps for underground use" - WIs No. 4-22-02, Issue 1, March 1991. WRc.

102. "Specification for elastomeric seals for joints in pipework and pipelines" - BS 2494:1990. BSI.

103. "Guidance for the selection, properties and use of elastomeric seals and sealing components" - IGN No. 4-40-02, Issue 1, July 1989. WRc.

104. "Selection, properties, storage and installation requirements for elastomeric seals and sealing rings" - IGN No. 4-40-01, Issue 2, August 1986. WRc.

105. "Specification for suitability of metallic materials for use in contact with water intended for human consumption with regard to their effect on the quality of the water" - DD 201: 1991. BSI.

106. "Suitability of non-metallic products for use in contact with water intended for human consumption with regard to their effect on the quality of the water: Part 1. Specification" - BS 6920: Part 1: 1990. BSI.

107. "Requirements for the testing of non-metallic products for use in contact with potable water" - IGN No. 5-01-02, Issue 6, 1992. WRc.

108. "Working party on the design and construction of pipe sewers" - DoE Circular 16/72, 23 February 1972. HMSO.

109. "Working party on the design and construction of underground pipe sewers" - DoE Water Authorities Circular 1/74, 5 April 1974. DoE.

110. "Granular bedding materials for buried pipelines" - IGN 4-08, April 1980. NWC.

111. "Bedding and sidefill materials for buried pipelines" - IGN 4-08-01, Issue 4, February 1994. WRc.

112. "Specification for bedding and sidefill materials for buried pipelines" - WIs No. 4-08-02, Issue 1, February 1994. WRc.

113. "Specification for precast and in situ ferrocement" - WIs No. 4-12-06, Issue 1, January 1990. WRc.

114. "Specification for non-circular polyethylene sewer linings" - WIs No. 4-32-10, Issue 1, January 1990. WRc.

115. "Precast concrete pipes and ancillary concrete products: Part 200. Specification for unreinforced and reinforced manholes and soakaways of circular cross-section" - BS 5911: Part 200: 1994. BSI.

116. "Manhole steps: Specification for plastics encapsulated manhole steps" - BS 1247: Part 2: 1990. BSI.

117. "Manhole steps: Specification for aluminium manhole steps" - BS 1247: Part 3: 1991. BSI.

118. "Specification for polypropylene encapsulated steps for use in manholes and access chambers" - WIs No. 4-33-01, Issue 1, January 1990. BSI.

119. "Specification for the Reinstatement of Openings in Highways: A code of practice approved by the Secretaries of State for Transport, Wales and Scotland under Sections 71 and 130 of the New Roads and Street Works Act" - HAUC, June 1992. HMSO.

120. "Testing aggregates: Method for determination of frost heave" - BS 812: Part 124: 1989. BSI.

121. "Standard test methods for flexible cellular materials made from olefin coploymers" - ASTM D3575: 1991. ASTM.

122. "Specification for building and construction joint sealants" - Wls No. 4-60-01, Issue 1, March 1991. WRc.

123. "Performance of sealant concrete joints in wet conditions: Volume 1. Results of a laboratory testing programme - Main results and discussion" - CIRIA Technical Note TN144, 1992. CIRIA.

124. "The Street Works (Reinstatement) Regulations 1992" - S.I. 1992 No. 1689. HMSO.

125. "Environmental Protection Act 1990" - Chapter 43. HMSO.

126. "Code of practice for demolition" - BS 6187: 1982. BSI.

127. "Code of practice for foundations" - BS 8004: 1986. BSI.

128. "Piling specification for the water industry" - WAA working group draft, April 1989. Restricted circulation.

129. "Concrete: Part 1. Guide to specifying concrete" - BS 5328: Part 1: 1991. BSI.

130. "Concrete: Part 2. Methods for specifying concrete mixes" - BS 5328: Part 2: 1991. BSI.

131. "Concrete: Part 3. Specification for the procedures to be used in producing and transporting concrete" - BS 5328: Part 3: 1991. BSI.

132. "Concrete: Part 4. Specification for the procedures to be used in sampling, testing and assessing compliance of concrete" - BS 5328: Part 4: 1991. BSI.

133. "Code of practice for design of concrete structures for retaining aqueous liquids" - BS 8007: 1987. BSI.

134. "Inadequate site investigation" - Report by the Ground Board of ICE, February 1991. Thomas Telford.

135. "Regina v British Rail" - Judgement of the High Court in Edinburgh, 27 May 1980.

136. "Pipe laying principles" - National Building Studies Special Report 35, 1964. HMSO.

137. "Simplified tables of external loads on buried pipelines" - Transport and Road Research Laboratory, 1986. HMSO.

138. "Precast concrete pipes and ancillary concrete products: Part 110. Specification for ogee pipes and fittings (including perforated)" - BS 5911: Part 110: 1992. BSI.

139. "Sewerage: Part 1. Guide to new sewerage construction" - BS 8005: Part 1: 1987. BSI.

140.   "A review of the practice and recommendations in making connections to pipe sewers" - Occasional Technical Paper No. 1, August 1978. NWC.

141.   "Code of practice for microtunnelling" - Second edition, November 1991. Yorkshire Water plc.

142.   "Microtunnelling advances in the UK" - H White and C E Tregoing, No-Dig '92, Paris, France, 12-14 October 1992.

143.   "Sewerage: Part 3. Guide to planning and construction of sewers in tunnel" - BS 8005: Part 3: 1989. BSI.

144.   "Code of best practice for the installation of pipe jacks and microtunnels" - PJA, in preparation. PJA.

145.   "Code of practice for use of masonry: Part 3. Materials and components, design and workmanship" - BS 5628: Part 3: 1985. BSI.

146.   "Water mains rehabilitation manual" - WRc, 1989. WRc/WAA.

147.   "Yorkshire Water Authority v Sir Alfred McAlpine & Son (Northern) Limited" - Judgement of the High Court in London, 25 June 1985.

148.   "Standard Specification for Water and Sewerage Schemes: Third Edition" - SADWSS/DoE for Northern Ireland, November 1989. WRc.